A Demo a Day

A Year of Chemical Demonstrations

Borislaw Bilash II

George R. Gross

John K. Koob

Published by:

FLINN SCIENTIFIC, INC.
P.O. Box 219
Batavia, IL 60510
(630) 879-6900

ISBN 1–877991–36–8

Printed in the United States of America.

Chemistry Pledge

I pledge allegiance to the chart of
the Periodic Table of Elements,
and to the Atomic Theory for which it stands.
One concept, under Mendeleev,
for observations and experimentation for all.

Table of Contents

Chapter 10 — Atomic Structure & Bonding

Chapter 11 — Periodicity

Chapter 12 — Solutions & Colloids

Chapter 13 — Acids/Bases

Chapter 14 — Kinetics

Chapter 15 — Equilibrium

Chapter 16 — Redox

Chapter 17 — Electrochemistry

Chapter 18 — Polymer Chemistry

About the Authors

BORISLAW BILASH II, Ed.M.

Currently Science Supervisor and teacher at Summit High School in Summit, NJ where he teaches Chemistry, Physics and Physical Science. Born in Winnipeg, Manitoba, Canada, he received his B.Sc. from the University of Manitoba in Winnipeg in 1986 and his Ed.M. from Rutgers University—New Brunswick, NJ in 1993. Borislaw began his teaching career at Queen of Peace High School in North Arlington, NJ in 1986, where he taught Honors Chemistry and Physical Science. Borislaw served as Science Department Chairperson (1990–1993). He has also taught Chemistry and Physics in the INROADS program at Rutgers University—Newark and Physics in the Upward Bound program at Essex County College also in Newark.

Borislaw has also completed work in curriculum development for The Manitoba Department of Education and has done editing for Silver, Burdett, Ginn. Inc. of Morristown, NJ. Borislaw is an active member of ACS—North Jersey Teachers Affiliates, NSTA, NJSTA, AAPT and a founding member of New Jersey's Chemistry Teachers' Alliance Group. He has presented chemistry demonstrations at various schools in New Jersey and Pennsylvania, at the New Jersey Science Convention, New Jersey ACS Chemistry Day and during National Chemistry Week. Borislaw, a New Jersey Governor Fellow of Science, has been honored three times with The Queen of Peace High School Principal's Creative Teaching Award and has been listed twice in *Who's Who Among America's Teachers.*

GEORGE R. GROSS, Ed. D.

George R. Gross, Ed.D., a 31-year teaching veteran is currently teaching AP chemistry and ChemCon at Union High School, NJ. Born in Paterson, NJ, he received his BA in 1964 and MA in 1966 from Montclair State University, Upper Montclair, NJ, an MS from Syracuse University in 1970 and his Ed.D. in 1977 from Rutgers—The State University, New Brunswick, NJ. He has been an active member of the CHEM5 Team of the Woodrow Wilson TORCH program since 1987. Involved in the Project Acceleration Program at Seton Hall University since its inception and active in the ACS as councilor and alternate councilor. He has served as president of NJSTA, chair of the ACS–North Jersey Teachers Affiliates, founder of the ChemTAG group, served on the New Jersey Science Convention for 19 years and as chairman of CHEMED '85. He has been recognized by *Who's Who Among America's Teachers,* the CMA, ACS North Jersey (1986), received the NJ Presidential Award in 1983, an Alumni Citation from Montclair State University in 1989, and a Citation Scroll from NJSTA in 1982. Most recently he was chosen to occupy the Chair of Mathematics and Science in Union Township, NJ and received the Homer J. Hall Award from the NJ Institute of Chemists.

JOHN K. KOOB, B.S.

Currently Science Department Chair at Queen of Peace High School, North Arlington, NJ. Born in Carlstadt, NJ, he received his B.S. in 1968 from Montclair State College, Montclair, NJ. He has taught Chemistry, Advanced Chemistry, Physics, Earth Science, Algebra and Trigonometry over a span of 26 years. John began teaching in 1968 at East Rutherford (NJ) High School, and moved to Queen of Peace High School in 1970. He is a founding member of the New Jersey Chemistry Teachers' Alliance Group (ChemTAG), and is an active member of NSTA. John has presented demonstrations on many occasions at the New Jersey Science Convention, New Jersey ACS Chemistry Day and during National Chemistry Week. Awarded the Queen of Peace High School Principal's Creative Teaching Award on four occasions, John has also been listed twice in *Who's Who Among America's Teachers.*

Acknowledgments

The demonstrations included in this series were collected from various sources including demonstration books compiled by such wizards as Hubert Alyea, Bassam Shakhashiri, Irwin Telesnick, Lee Summerlin, Christine L. Borgford, and James and Julie Ealy. Some demonstrations were extracted from the pages of *The Journal of Chemical Education,* while others were drawn from the presentations of colleagues at our local New Jersey Chemistry Teachers' Alliance Group (ChemTAG) meetings. Woodrow Wilson Fellowship TORCH Institutes and The Institute for Chemical Education must be singled out as having served as a key source for many of the demonstrations and ideas. Both of these institutions greatly influence our work. We have tried to provide references, where possible, to previous versions or the source of our inspiration. We apologize if we overlooked a reference.

It is our intention to provide teachers with an organized collection of demonstrations which have been tested in our own classrooms. It is with great appreciation that we acknowledge the contributions our colleagues have made in producing this collection of demonstrations. All of these demonstrations have been presented by fellow "ChemTAGers" or by the authors at ChemTAG's Demo Den at the New Jersey Science Convention during the last few years. We have gained much insight by having teachers share the experiences they had in using these demonstrations in their classrooms. We hope that you will find this book helpful and that it will contribute to making your teaching effective and the chemistry relevant to your students.

Lastly, we wish to express our gratitude to Mark Meszaros, Staff Chemist at Flinn Scientific, who spent many hours meticulously reviewing these demonstrations. His advice and contributions have been very helpful. Thanks Mark!

Borislaw N. Bilash II
George R. Gross
John K. Koob

Millburn, NJ
March 1995

Safety Procedures

Chemical demonstrators must:

1. Know the properties of the chemicals and chemical reactions involved in all demonstrations presented.

2. Comply with all local rules and regulations.

3. Wear appropriate eye protection for all chemical demonstrations.

4. Warn the members of the audience to cover their ears whenever a loud noise is anticipated.

5. Plan the demonstration so that harmful quantities of noxious gases (e.g., NO_2, SO_2, H_2S) do not enter the local air supply.

6. Provide safety shield protection whenever there is the slightest possibility that a container, its fragments, or its contents could be propelled with sufficient force to cause personal injury.

7. Arrange to have a fire extinguisher at hand whenever the slightest possibility of fire exists.

8. **Not** taste or encourage spectators to taste any nonfood substances.

9. **Not** use demonstrations in which parts of the human body are placed in danger (such as placing dry ice in the mouth or dipping hands into liquid nitrogen).

10. **Not** use "open" containers of volatile, toxic substances (e.g., benzene, CCl_4, CS_2, formaldehyde) without adequate ventilation as provided by fume hoods.

11. Provide written procedure, hazard, and disposal information for each demonstration whenever the audience is encouraged to repeat the demonstration.

12. Arrange for appropriate waste containers for and subsequent disposal of materials harmful to the environment.

Disposal Procedures

The disposal procedures included in this book are based on the Suggested Laboratory Chemical Disposal Procedures found in the *Flinn Scientific Catalog/Reference Manual.* The disposal procedures are only suggestions—do not use these procedures if you are not comfortable with the chemistry. Do not use these procedures without first consulting with your local government regulatory officials.

Many of the demonstrations produce small volumes of aqueous solutions that can be flushed down the drain with excess water. Do not use this procedure if your drains empty into groundwater through a septic system or into a storm sewer. Local regulations may be more strict on drain disposal than the practices suggested in this book and in the *Flinn Scientific Catalog/Reference Manual.* You must determine what types of disposal procedures are permitted in your area—contact your local authorities.

Any suggested disposal method that includes "discard in the trash" requires your involvement. Make sure that the material is no longer reactive, is placed in a suitable container (plastic bag or bottle), and is in accordance with local landfill regulations. Please do not inadvertently perform any extra demonstrations due to unpredictable chemical reactions occurring in your trash can— think before you throw!

Lastly, please read all the narratives if you attempt any Suggested Laboratory Chemical Disposal Method found in the *Flinn Scientific Catalog/Reference Manual.*

Solution Preparations

When preparing acid solutions, always **ADD ACID (AA)** to water! A great amount of heat is liberated when an acid (or strong base) is added to water. The temperatures of the solution will rise rapidly. In fact, the solution may rise so fast that the solution will boil and possibly spatter a strong acidic (or basic) solution. Consider immersing your mixing vessel in a bucket of ice to control the solution temperature. Cooling the reaction vessel is particularly important when preparing sodium hydroxide and sulfuric acid solutions. For all solutions, always add the acid (or base) to water very slowly while stirring continuously.

Most acid or base solutions are available premixed from Flinn Scientific but can also be made from concentrated reagents and distilled water using the following recipes.

Reagent	Solution Concentration	Reagent Required for	
		100 mL	500 mL
Acetic Acid, Glacial **(17.4 Molar)**	0.1 M	0.6 mL	2.9 mL
	1.0 M	5.7 mL	28.5 mL
	2.0 M	11.5 mL	57.0 mL
	3.0 M	17.2 mL	86.0 mL
	6.0 M	34.5 mL	172.0 mL
Hydrochloric Acid, Conc. **(12.1 Molar)**	0.1 M	0.8 mL	4.1 mL
	1.0 M	8.3 mL	41.3 mL
	2.0 M	16.5 mL	82.6 mL
	3.0 M	24.8 mL	124.0 mL
	6.0 M	49.6 mL	248.0 mL
Nitric Acid, Conc. **(15.8 Molar)**	0.1 M	0.6 mL	3.1 mL
	1.0 M	5.3 mL	31.6 mL
	2.0 M	12.7 mL	63.3 mL
	3.0 M	19.0 mL	95.0 mL
	6.0 M	38.0 mL	190.0 mL
Sulfuric Acid, Conc. **(18.0 Molar)**	0.1 M	0.6 mL	2.8 mL
	1.0 M	6.6 mL	27.8 mL
	2.0 M	11.1 mL	55.6 mL
	3.0 M	16.7 mL	83.3 mL
	6.0 M	33.3 mL	166.7 mL
	9.0 M	50.0 mL	250.0 mL
Sodium Hydroxide, Pellets **(40 g/mole)**	0.1 M	0.4 g	2.0 g
	0.35 M	1.4 g	7.0 g
	1.0 M	4.0 g	20.0 g
	2.0 M	8.0 g	40.0 g
	6.0 M	24.0 g	120.0 g
Ammonium Hydroxide, Conc. **(14.8 Molar)**	0.1 M	.7 mL	3.4 mL
	1.0 M	6.8 mL	33.8 mL
	6.0 M	40.5 mL	202.7 mL

Several chemical demonstrations in *A Demo A Day* require saturated solutions. The following table provides approximate saturation levels.

Reagent	Formula	g/100 mL H$_2$O
Barium Hydroxide	Ba(OH)$_2$ · 8H$_2$O	6
Calcium Acetate	Ca(C$_2$H$_3$O$_2$)$_2$ · H$_2$O	44
Calcium Hydroxide	Ca(OH)$_2$	0.2
Calcium Sulfate	CaSO$_4$ · 2H$_2$O	0.2
Cupric Sulfate	CuSO$_4$ · 5H$_2$O	22.0
Limewater	Ca(OH)$_2$	0.2
Magnesium Hydroxide	Mg(OH)$_2$	0.1
Manganese Sulfate	MnSO$_4$	59
Sodium Bicarbonate	NaHCO$_3$	10
Sodium Sulfate	Na$_2$SO$_4$	26
Sodium Tetraborate	Na$_2$B$_4$O$_7$ · 10H$_2$O	2
Strontium Hydroxide	Sr(OH)$_2$ · 8H$_2$O	15
Zinc Sulfate	ZnSO$_4$ · 7H$_2$O	55

Demonstration Supplies

Demonstration Kits: Flinn Scientific has assembled many popular demonstrations into Chemistry Demonstration Kits. These kits come complete with all the chemicals and solutions already prepared to perform the demonstration seven times. Many more demonstrations from this book will be turned into kits in the near future. Look in your current *Flinn Catalog/Reference Manual* or call Flinn at 1-800-452-1261 for available kits.

Chemicals & Supplies: The most common reason that a demonstration does not work is due to old or poor quality chemicals. Use fresh chemicals, prepare fresh solutions and use clean glassware to assure good quality demonstrations.

Dry Ice: Dry ice is available from a number of sources or can be produced in your lab using a dry ice maker. For a source of dry ice, look in your yellow pages under gases, (carbon dioxide) or call a local meat packer or ice cream shop. Frost bite is a real danger when handling dry ice, always wear cloth or insulated gloves. Dry ice can be stored in a Styrofoam® cooler or wrapped in newspaper—never in a closed container.

Liquid Nitrogen: Liquid nitrogen (N_2) is used in some spectacular demonstrations but must be handled with care. Liquid nitrogen is at –196 °C and will cause serious frostbite in a short period of time. To protect yourself and your students, please observe the following safety precautions whenever you use liquid nitrogen.

- Wear safety glasses at all times.

- Wear insulating gloves when handling liquid nitrogen.

- Do not allow liquid nitrogen to touch your body.

- Do not touch anything immersed in liquid nitrogen until it has warmed up to room temperature.

- Be careful never to overfill or spill liquid nitrogen from any container.

- Do not move liquid nitrogen in a manner that causes splashing.

- The gas, while non-toxic, can asphyxiate through displacement of oxygen. Use it only in well ventilated areas.

- Never store liquid nitrogen in a container with a tight fitting lid.

- Liquid nitrogen may be obtained from a number of sources. Try a local college or university, hospital or dermatologist, frozen food/meat processors and distributors, research labs, or welding supply stores.

- Use a Dewar to transport or store liquid nitrogen. Some suppliers of liquid nitrogen will loan or rent 10–20 L Dewar flasks. A stainless steel thermos bottle can be used as an inexpensive Dewar but, do not use the screw cap—stuff a paper towel into the top as a cover. The screw cap may seal the thermos causing it to explode! A cheap Dewar that will work for short periods of time is a half of the polystyrene foam containers used for shipping acids.

Chapter 1

Introducing Chemistry

Nitric Acid Acts Upon Copper — The First Demo

A historical demonstration of the wonders of discovery in chemistry.

Application | Observation • Scientific Method • Redox

Theory | The reaction is $Cu(s) + 4HNO_3(aq) \rightarrow Cu(NO_3)_2(aq) + 2NO_2(g) + 2H_2O(l)$

The reaction is rapid and exothermic. If a slower reaction is desired, dilute the nitric acid to a concentration of 8 molar.

Materials | Nitric acid, 15 M, HNO_3 (5 mL)
Glass Petri dish
Pennies (2–3)

Safety Precautions | Nitric acid is corrosive; strong oxidant; toxic by inhalation; avoid contact with acetic acid and readily oxidized substances. The gases produced are quite irritating, establish adequate ventilation. If adequate ventilation is not available perform the demonstration in a 1000-mL flask with a damp towel placed over the top. The gases will dissolve into the water. Wear chemical splash goggles, chemical-resistant gloves and a chemical-resistant apron.

Demonstration | Begin by introducing a discussion about the field of chemistry followed by an introduction of Ira Remsen (1846–1927). Remsen founded the chemistry department at Johns Hopkins University and initiated the first chemical research center in the United States. The following is an excerpt from his memoirs. It should be read as the demonstration is performed:

While reading a textbook on chemistry, I came upon a statement "nitric acid acts upon copper". I was getting tired of reading such absurd stuff and I determined to see what it meant. Copper was more or less familiar to me, for copper pennies were then in use. I had seen a bottle marked "nitric acid" on a table in the doctor's office where I was then "doing time"! I did not know its peculiarities but I was getting on and likely to learn. The spirit of adventure was upon me. Having nitric acid and copper, I had only to learn what the words "act upon" meant. Then the statement, "nitric acid acts upon copper" would be something more than mere words.

All was still. In the interest of knowledge I was even willing to sacrifice one of the few copper cents then in my possession. I put one of them on the table; opened the bottle marked "nitric acid"; poured some of the liquid on the copper; and prepared to make an observation.

Place the pennies in a Petri dish and pour the nitric acid over them.

But what was this wonderful thing which I beheld? The cent was already changed, and it was no small change either. A greenish blue liquid foamed and fumed over the cent and over the table. The air in the neighborhood of the performance became dark and red. A great colored cloud arose. This was disagreeable and suffocating—how should I stop this? I tried to get rid of the objectionable mess by picking it up and throwing it out of the window, which I had meanwhile opened. I learned another fact—nitric acid not only acts upon copper but it acts upon fingers. The pain led to yet another unpremeditated experiment. I drew my fingers across my trousers and another fact was discovered. Nitric acid also acts upon trousers.

Taking everything into consideration, that was the most impressive experiment, and relatively, probably the most costly experiment I have ever performed. I tell of it even now with interest. It was a revelation to me. It resulted in a desire on my part to learn more about that remarkable kind of action. Plainly the only way to learn about it was to see its results, to experiment, to work in the laboratory.

Disposal

The pennies may be rinsed with water and reused. Copper nitrate solution may be flushed down the drain with excess water.

Reference

Getman, F. H. *J. Chem. Ed.* **1940,** 9.

Observation of a Burning Candle

A quick, clean and simple demonstration to develop observation skills.

Application	Observation • Scientific Method • Analysis
Theory	Perhaps one of the most important skills of the chemistry student is observation. Knowledge of the distinction between an observation and an inference is critical to success in the laboratory and also in the critical thinking necessary for problem solving. It has been said by some that there are more than 50 actual observations that may be made while observing a burning candle. Major emphasis here should be on the observations: "Black smoke rises from the flame"; rather than the inference: "There is carbon rising from the flame". No basis exists for the beginner for the latter statement.
Materials	Candle Matches
Safety Precautions	Keep flammables from the open flame and burn only on a fireproof surface.
Preparation	Prepare work area as described above. Be certain that all students have paper, etc. If lights are dimmed, allow enough light to facilitate writing and note taking. Several candles may be used, although one large enough to be seen by all is best.
Demonstration	Describe the differences between an observation and an inference. Light the candle and then dim the lights. Permit adequate time (about 5 minutes) for the collection of observations. Go around the class and have each student read one different "observation" and analyze each.
Disposal	None required. Save candle for future use.

Potato Candle

The importance of observation is demonstrated while grabbing students' attention.

Application	Observation • Scientific Method
Theory	The oils found in nut meats are combustible.
Materials	Potato (white Idaho baking type works best) Apple corer Brazil nut (seems to work best) Knife or single edge razor blade Matches
Safety Precautions	Don't cut yourself. Remind your students that materials found in lab should never be eaten. This, however, is a very carefully controlled demonstration.
Preparation	Use the apple corer to cut a cylindrical "candle" out of the potato. Cut a bit off of the top and bottom so it sits flat. Soak in lemon juice to prevent yellowing. Cut the Brazil nut so that you have a thin "wick" about 2 to 3 cm long. Cut an "X" in the top of the "candle" and insert the "wick". It will burn for about 3 to 5 minutes.
Demonstration	This demo is best done near the end of the class period. Simply tell students that you have a candle. Ask them to observe and write down their observations. Turn the room lights out, light the candle and let them start. Blow out the candle before it burns out, and then ask students to read their observations out loud. Someone will see the wax melting, the braided wick, the carbon dioxide and water vapor coming off. Remind them about observation and interpretation and how they might have to change their conclusions on the basis of new evidence.
	If you have this timed correctly, there will only be about one minute left in the period. Now eat the candle and walk out of the room—never tell them what it was!!! This will convince your classes that you are an eccentric. There is a lot to be said for this. The next class, ask what information might lead them to believe that it was not a normal candle. (It crunched.) Explain how new information constantly leads to changes in science. (Note: You might want to use a banana instead, it tastes better.)
Disposal	None required.
Reference	Lee Marek, Naperville North High School, Naperville, IL, at Woodrow Wilson Chem 8 Institute.

The Scientific Method

Investigate the components of the scientific method by solving a real problem.

Application	Observation • Scientific Method
Theory	When confronted with a failure of a common device, the scientific method is often pressed into service. Here students are confronted with a lamp (or other device) that will not work when the switch is turned on. Careful observation, hypothesizing, testing and finally construction of a conclusion and solution to the problem results with success.
Materials	An electric lamp A spare bulb (or some other similar device available in the classroom)
Safety Precautions	Normal precautions for the device chosen should be followed.
Preparation	Obtain the lamp or other device to be used. Having several different devices for several classes will avoid duplication and students being "prepared" for the activity. Plan ahead as to what problems you will build into the device. Plug out; bulb loose; bulb burned out; switch off; or some combination of these.
Demonstration	Bring out the lamp and place it on the laboratory table or lecture desk without a lot of attention or have it in place before the students arrive. Hang the plug over the edge, out of sight.
	Briefly outline what you plan to do without telling all. "Today we will investigate the scientific method and use it to solve a real problem."
	Attempt to turn on the lamp. Pretend to be disturbed that it does not light and ask for suggestions. Most students will offer suggestions, unsolicited. Try the suggestions one at a time. You might reverse each attempt and return to original conditions to make the exercise more interesting.
	Students will soon realize what is happening, that more than one problem may exist, that you are returning each attempt to original states, or that there may actually be more than one problem with the lamp.
	Allow about 5 minutes for this followed by a 3 to 5 minute summary on the board listing the steps that were followed to solve the problem.
Disposal	None required.

Chapter 2

Operations and Measurement in Chemistry

A Simulated "Acid in Your Eye" Accident

Show students what will happen if they fail to wear safety goggles in a lab.

Application	Safety • Eyes
Theory	An acid solution of sufficient concentration will denature or coagulate the protein, albumin, in a raw egg white.
Materials	Raw eggs (whites only), 1 or more Petri dish Strong acid, 6 M, HCl, H_2SO_4, or HNO_3 Sodium bicarbonate solution, $NaHCO_3$, saturated Dropper bottle or pipet Overhead projector Permanent marker
Safety Precautions	All of the acid solutions are corrosive to skin and eyes and toxic by inhalation and ingestion. Wear chemical splash goggles, chemical-resistant gloves and a chemical-resistant apron.
Preparation	Use a permanent marker to draw a large "eye" on the bottom of the petri dish. Prepare saturated sodium bicarbonate solution (10 g in 100 mL H_2O).
Demonstration	Place the egg white in the Petri dish, and place on the overhead. Discuss the similarity of the transparent egg white to the eye's pupil. Place several drops of the acid onto the egg white. It will immediately become opaque.
	Some students might suggest that you can "UNDO" the damage. You might ask them how to "UNCOOK" an egg. Try gently rinsing the spots with a baking soda solution. It cannot be made transparent again!
	Note: The denaturation is equally dramatic with NaOH solution. Even when neutralized, the opaque area will continue to expand for several hours.
Disposal	The egg white can be discarded in the trash.
References	Lynn Higgins, Proviso East High School, Maywood, IL.
	Lee Marek, Naperville North High School, Naperville, IL, at Woodrow Wilson Chem 8 Institute.

Contact Lens Demo

Show students why it is unsafe to wear contact lenses in a chemical laboratory.

Application   Safety • Eyes

Theory   Many universities and industrial laboratories prohibit the wearing of contact lenses by occupants in order to protect them from danger. There are many reasons for this. Some contacts are known to absorb vapors from the air, and in some cases, dissolve them right on the eye of the wearer. The major reason centers on the behavior of the lens if something were to splash in the eye. Instead of being a "last resort" protector, the lens acts to bring the unwanted material to the location where it could do the most damage, the pupil. This can be demonstrated using an idea borrowed from slide preparation in biology.

Materials   Overhead projector
Acetate film (2 sheets)
Permanent marker
Dark food coloring
Wash bottle
Eyedropper

Safety Precautions   Always follow laboratory safety rules while performing demonstrations.

Preparation   Draw the front profile of an eyeball on one sheet of film. Cut a circular "contact lens" from the other sheet of film.

Demonstration   Place the large film on the overhead stage. Position the "contact lens" over the pupil that you have drawn. Put 1 to 2 drops of food coloring on the edge of the "contact". Observe how capillary action draws the mixture under the "lens". Use the wash bottle to try to wash the coloring out. Blot with a paper towel. Observe that some of the colored solution remains under the "lens".

Disposal   None required.

References   Bob Lewis, Downers Grove North High School, Downers Grove, IL, at Woodrow Wilson Chemistry 5 Institute.

John Brodemus, Richards High School, Oak Lawn, IL.

Fire Extinguisher Demo

The operation and function of fire extinguishers is one common safety technique that should be demonstrated in the laboratory.

Application
Safety • Combustion Reactions • Limiting Reactant • Activation Energy

Theory
Fires require fuel, a heat source and a supply of oxygen. Removal of any one of these is usually sufficient to extinguish the fire. An easy demonstration of the concept of limiting reactants occurs when either the fuel or the oxygen supply is removed. Removing or lowering the temperature lowers the activation energy and the reaction cannot proceed or continue.

Materials
Candle
Watch glass or metal pie pan
Carbon dioxide, CO_2
Paper towels
Spray bottle with mister
Sand
100-mL Beaker

Safety Precautions
Do not overdo the size of the fire. Work on a non-flammable surface and have a fire extinguisher handy. Temporarily disable the room's smoke detectors but be sure to reconnect upon completion of lab. Wear chemical splash goggles and always follow laboratory safety rules while performing demonstrations.

Preparation
Set up a source for CO_2 ahead of time. Generate CO_2 from baking soda and vinegar or marble chips and hydrochloric acid in a large beaker. CO_2 is also available from a cylinder of carbon dioxide, a carbon dioxide fire extinguisher, or evaporating dry ice. Remember that this gas is heavier (more dense) than air and will stay in a partially covered, deep beaker until needed.

Afix a candle to the inside bottom of a 400-mL beaker as a fire source and have a small amount of paper on a watch glass or metal pie pan as a second fire source. Fill the spray bottle with water. Moisten several paper towels with water.

Demonstration
Light the candle in the beaker. Generate carbon dioxide in a large beaker. Pour the carbon dioxide, not the contents, of the large beaker into the smaller one with the burning candle. Re-light the candle and place one of the wet paper towels over the top of the beaker. Light the paper on the watch glass and mist the air above the fire with water. Do not spray directly onto the fire. Light a second batch of dry paper and place another of the moistened towels over it. Light a third batch of paper and pour sand directly onto the burning paper.

Disposal
All of the materials should be allowed to cool and then discarded in the trash.

Graphing — An Introductory Demo

Introduce graphing with an actual demonstration of data collection and treatment.

Application	Data Collection • Graphing
Theory	Hands-on preparation and interpretation of data in graph format will enable the students to become involved and to better understand the aspects of data collection and presentation. A preparatory demo such as this eliminates some of the lecture/text exercises commonly utilized.
Materials	Overhead projector Projectable graph coordinates (or chalkboard and graph axes) Collectable data: entering students; pre- and post-1982 pennies; substances for collecting density data Appropriate equipment such as cylinders, balance, meter sticks, bathroom scale
Safety Precautions	Wear chemical splash goggles and always follow laboratory safety rules while performing demonstrations.
Preparation	Decide what will be graphed and set it up before the class arrives so students may begin gathering data immediately. *Note: Students are not preparing graphs. This is a demonstration and student participation activity.* Collect pennies if they are to be used. Mount a meter stick for measuring heights of students as they enter. Pour liquid samples into cylinders. This is not a measurement exercise. Have appropriate solid samples if these are to be used. Don't make it complicated or difficult.
Demonstration	Begin collecting data as students enter. Collect 5 to 7 sets of data points. List data on overhead or chalkboard. Prepare graph Interpret graphing process and advantages. Density measurements and pennies make good graphs. Student height and weight data are not clearly graphable as a regular variable.
Disposal	None required.

Number Line

Give students a visual representation of exponential notation.

Application	Scientific Notation • Logarithmic Scales
Theory	Distances are used to demonstrate relationships between powers of ten.
Materials	Clothesline (8 to 10 meters) Clothespins (10) Index cards (10)
Safety Precautions	Wear chemical splash goggles and always follow laboratory safety rules while performing demonstrations.
Preparation	Mark separate index cards with the number 0 in red, 1, 2, and 3 in blue, 10^0, 10^1, 10^2, and 10^3 in green, 10^{-1}, and 10^{-2} in black. Use large markers. Tie the clothesline lengthwise across your classroom. Have it hanging there when the students come into the room, with the number 0 hanging about one-sixth of the way from one end, and the number 1 about 8 to 10 cm toward the longer side. You may want to attach the cards to the clothespins permanently by gluing.
Demonstration	Ask the students how many have studied scientific notation previously. Tell them that this rope is a number line. Have a student come up and pin the number 2 on the line where he/she thinks it should be. Have another student put the number 3 on the line. Most kids get this, if not, go see your math people immediately!
	Now the fun starts. Have another student put 10^1 on the line where he/she thinks it should be. Don't help, but let the others in the class help if you want. This gets them to think about the system. When all are happy, give a student 10^2. Then another gets 10^3. (This could be time to get even!!)
	Next comes 10^0. This should be easy, but it's not—because most kids forgot this or never really understood it.
	The last part even burns some math teachers, the "–" powers. Give someone 10^{-1} and someone else 10^{-2}. You will be amazed where the numbers end up. (They should be between 1 and zero.)
	Now you can review scientific notation, what it means, and why we use it in science.
Disposal	None required.
Reference	Lee Marek, Naperville North High School, Naperville, IL, at Woodrow Wilson Chem 8 Institute.

Precision or Accuracy?

Illustrate that measurements that are accurate are not necessarily precise and that precise measurements are not necessarily accurate.

Application | Accuracy • Precision • Measurement • Systematic Error • Observation

Theory | Accuracy of a measurement refers to how close a measurement is to the true value of what is measured. If a piece of string, which is truly 50 cm in length, is measured to be only 49 cm or as much as 51 cm, the measured value is considered inaccurate. The measurement is only accurate if measured to be 50 cm.

Precision of a measurement refers to the reproducibility of the measurement. If for example, the same string is consistently measured by ten people to be 49 cm, one would say that the measurement is precise, because it is reproducible. The measurement is not accurate because the true value is 50 cm; but it is precise, as it was reproduced over and over again.

Yet another example involves a number of arrows shot at a target. An accurate shot would place the arrow at the center of the bull's eye. An example of a precise shot would place the arrows next to the other arrows in a group. This group of arrows may be found anywhere on the target. This group may or may not be located over the bull's eye. Regardless of their exact position, with respect to the bull's eye, if the arrows are grouped together, one would refer to the precision of the shots. If one of these arrows would by chance deviate from this group, and land on the bull's eye, one would refer to this shot as pure luck!

In science it is reproducibility that is important, rather than luck. Reproducibility can be fined-tuned and may result in accuracy; however accuracy does not always bring precision.

Materials | Meter sticks (2)   Hand saw

Safety Precautions | Always follow laboratory safety rules while performing demonstrations.

Preparation | Carefully saw off the first centimeter from one of the meter sticks.

Demonstration | Invite two students to measure the length of some object, perhaps the length of a lab bench. Give one student a regular meter stick and the other the shortened meter stick. Take care that no one notices the defective meter stick. Have the students make their measurements and then return to their seats. Ask each student to tell the class what they measured the object to be. They should not agree with each other (if measured correctly, their measurements are expected to be off by 1 cm). Invite two more students to measure the same item and then inform the class of their measurements. After a few measurements, the students should see that the measurements will always differ by 1 cm. Inform the students about the "short end of the stick" and discuss the differences between the precision and accuracy.

Disposal | None required.

Reference | Fraser, W. S. *Chemistry;* Addison Wesley: Menlo Park, CA, 1987; p 20.

Observation of a Density Column

A density column is used to distinguish between observations and inferences and improve problem solving skills.

Application	Observation • Inference • Physical Properties • Scientific Method
Theory	This is a substitution for the traditional burning candle demonstration.
	By using a density column, a new set of observations is presented. Emphasis should be on the observation; "the red liquid is on top of the blue liquid"; not the inference "the red liquid is lighter than the blue liquid".
Materials	Large cylinder, 500 or 1000-mL Variety of household items
Safety Precautions	Wear chemical splash goggles and always follow laboratory safety rules while performing demonstrations.
Preparation	Set up the density column in a large (500 or 1000-mL) cylinder. A household column is cheapest and easiest to obtain and set up. A suggested column is (top to bottom) cork, baby oil, paraffin, water (colored), rubber stopper, corn syrup, penny. Be especially careful to add liquids slowly to avoid cloudy interfaces. Pour slowly down the side of a tipped cylinder. Fill the cylinder so it is clearly visible to all students.
Demonstration	Place the column in front of the class so it is visible to all. Put on a light box or on the stage of the overhead projector for more light.
	Describe the differences between an observation and an inference.
	Permit adequate time for recording of observations, about 5 minutes.
	Go around the class permitting each student to read one observation and analyze each. Try mixing it up, go from back to front or some other new distribution of names called.
Disposal	The solids and liquids can be disposed of in the trash or by flushing down the drain with excess water.

A Rather Large Thermometer

A home-made thermometer is used to reinforce the concept of expansion and the construction and use of a thermometer.

Application | Thermal Expansion • Thermometers • Heat • Observation

Theory | When heated, the level of the liquid (Hg, alcohol, etc.) in a glass thermometer initially drops due to the fact that the thermal energy first must pass through the glass to reach the liquid. Glass has a relatively high specific heat capacity, with respect to the liquid. As a result, the glass will expand before enough heat is transferred into the liquid. Since the glass expands, the internal volume of the thermometer increases: thus the level of the liquid falls. The coefficient of expansion for solids, however, is generally smaller than for liquids, so once the liquid begins to absorb heat, it expands faster than the glass container, causing the level to rise.

Upon cooling a glass thermometer, heat leaves the glass faster than heat from the liquid can transfer through the glass, leaving the glass with a net loss of heat. As a result the glass contracts and the internal volume of the thermometer decreases: Thus the level of the liquid rises. Eventually, the liquid contracts faster than the glass, and the level falls as the temperature drops.

Materials

500-mL Erlenmeyer flask	Distilled water
One-hole rubber stopper	Food coloring
Glass tubing (1 meter)	Hot plate

Safety Precautions | Wear chemical splash goggles and always follow laboratory safety rules while performing demonstrations.

Preparation | Fit a one-hole rubber stopper with a 1 m long glass tube. Fill a 500-mL Erlenmeyer flask with colored water and affix the stopper. Be certain to add enough colored water to the flask, allowing the water to rest at a level halfway up the glass tube.

Demonstration | Place the thermometer on a preheated hot plate. Observe. Instead of the level of the liquid rising (as expected, due to thermal expansion), the level initially drops — then begins to rise. Have the students develop a possible explanation as to why the liquid dropped first, then began to rise in the thermometer.

Next, remove the thermometer from the hot plate and place it on a few drops of water sprinkled on a lab bench. Observe. Instead of the level of the liquid dropping (as expected, due to the contraction of the liquid), the level initially rises — then begins to drop. Again, discuss this phenomenon with your students.

Note: The construction of this thermometer was my first science project (when I was in third grade). I used a glass bottle, a cork, a plastic straw and red poster paint.
Borislaw Bilash

Disposal | None required.

Chapter 3

Properties of Matter

Elements, Mixtures and Compounds

Differences between the classes of matter using ordinary hardware are clearly demonstrated.

Application	Elements • Compounds • Mixtures
Theory	Elements consist of one kind of atom. Compounds consist of two or more different kinds of atoms that are chemically joined. Mixtures are two or more substances that are simply in the same container or material.
Materials	Small bolts or machine screws (6×32, 8×32, etc.) Hex nuts and washers to fit Plastic Petri dishes Overhead projector (optional)
Safety Precautions	Always follow laboratory safety rules while performing demonstrations.
Preparation	In Petri dishes, place just bolts or nuts or washers to represent elements. Make up two or three nut–bolt–washer assemblies, some others with just nut and bolt, and some others with nut, bolt and two washers. These represent compounds. Place in separate Petri dishes. Finally, in some other Petri dishes, place mixtures of nuts and washers, or bolts and washers or bolts with separate nuts. These represent mixtures. Make up as many as you want.
Demonstration	Number the Petri dishes. You might want to put them on a side table and have students look at them. Have students identify what class of matter they think is represented in each Petri dish. You might also want to do this on the overhead projector. Discuss the findings of the class with the students.
Disposal	None required, keep from year to year. You might want to seal the lids onto the Petri dishes to prevent spillage.
Reference	Ed Waterman, Rocky Mountain High School, Fort Collins, CO, at Woodrow Wilson Chem 8 Institute.

Immiscible Liquids

The concept of immiscibility of liquids is shown with this permanent setup.

Application	Physical Properties • Density • Surface Tension • Solubility
Theory	Solvation is determined by the compatibility of the solute and solvent. A simple rule is *like dissolves like*. If both solution components are nonpolar or if both are polar, solvation may occur. If solvation between two liquids does not occur, they will separate according to density.
Materials	One-liter plastic soda bottle Colorless baby oil (500 mL) Ethanol, C_2H_5OH, (250 mL) Food coloring of your choice 1,1,1-Trichloroethane, $C_2H_3Cl_3$, TCE (250 mL) Water
Safety Precautions	Ethanol is flammable and 1,1,1-Trichloroethane is irritating to eyes and tissue. Wear chemical splash goggles, chemical-resistant gloves and a chemical-resistant apron.
Preparation	In one of the bottles, mix the ethanol and 250 mL of water with the food coloring, then add the baby oil. In the other bottle put the TCE and the 500 mL of water with some food coloring. Cap tightly. Tape caps to discourage opening. If TCE is not available, use another non-miscible, dense liquid.
Demonstration	The baby oil–water bottle will have the colored aqueous layer at the bottom. Show it to the students, turn it upside down, shake it, and above all let the students play with it. Encourage them to try to duplicate it at home. (Remember those magic words "extra credit".) After a few days of having it available for the students to play with before class, replace it with the water–TCE bottle, which has the colored aqueous layer on top. See how long it takes for them to notice. Discuss why this one might be different.
Disposal	None required. Keep the bottles from year to year.
Reference	Jim Tarnowski, Avon High School, Avon, IN, at Woodrow Wilson Chem 5 Institute.

Uneven Liquids

Two liquids are introduced into a U-tube and the liquids do not reach the same level.

Application	Density • Specific Gravity • Solution Concentration
Theory	The demo is based on the density difference between salt water and fresh water. A saturated solution of sodium chloride is approximately 20% denser than fresh water. The interface between two solutions is very difficult to see.
Materials	Large glass U-tube, supported on ring stand Saturated solution of salt water Tap water Thistle tube or funnel Graduated cylinder with capacity similar to U-tube Small magnet
Safety Precautions	Wear chemical splash goggles and always follow laboratory safety rules while performing demonstrations.
Preparation	Make a large glass U-tube or, if necessary, connect two pieces of large diameter straight glass tubing with a 10 to 15 cm length of clear Tygon tubing. The whole assembly should be 40 to 50 cm high. Bigger is even better. Mix the saturated salt solution. Half fill the graduated cylinder with this solution. Carefully add the tap water to the cylinder. Do this slowly, and with the cylinder inclined, to avoid as much mixing as possible.
Demonstration	Have a student pour some water from the graduated cylinder into the U-tube. Point out that the liquid levels are the same on both sides. Explain to the students that water is a polar substance and that you are going to try to alter the height of one end by using a magnet to attract the water. Place a small magnet on top of the other side of the U-tube, and pour the rest of the liquid into the tube. The liquid level will be higher on the side with the magnet. Now ask the students what will happen if the magnet is removed. Remove it. The liquid levels do not change at all. Ask for suggestions for an explanation. You might also want to try having one end of the U-tube higher than the other to see if the students think that would be the cause of the unevenness. Challenge students to duplicate the results. (Remember the magic words "extra credit".)
Disposal	The solution can be flushed down the drain with excess water.
Reference	Zidick, Z. *J. Chem. Ed.* **1974**, *51*, A559.

Soap bubbles filled with hydrogen gas are ignited and explode.

Application	Gas Properties • Explosions • Density
Theory	A gas source is connected to a soap bubbling device producing gas-filled soap bubbles. Since hydrogen or methane gases are less dense than air, the bubbles rise. As the bubbles move aloft they are ignited and in turn explode. Glycerin is added to the soap mixture to improve the soap film strength.
Materials	Hydrogen or methane gas source Latex hose Plastic funnel, 10 cm diameter Commercial dishwashing detergent Glycerin Water Pie plate or other shallow container Ignition device*
Safety Precautions	Hydrogen gas is explosive, remove all ignition sources from the demonstration area. Warn students of explosive noise and instruct them to cup their hands over their ears to reduce the concussion of the explosion. Always use an ignition devise when igniting hydrogen-filled containers such as soap bubbles or balloons. Glycerin reacts violently with strong oxidants that may lead to an explosion; use with care. Wear chemical splash goggles, chemical-resistant gloves and a chemical-resistant apron. Propane bubbles do not rise.
Preparation	Prepare a soap solution by mixing 50 mL of commercial dishwashing detergent and 50 mL glycerin with 300 mL water.
	Attach a latex hose between the gas source and a plastic funnel. Secure the hose to the funnel with wire or duct tape if necessary.
	*An ignition device may be made by affixing a wooden splint or candle to the end of a meter stick. Never light a gas source container directly with a match.
Demonstration	Turn on gas. Immerse the bubbling device into a pan of soap solution and allow a soap bubble to form. Let the bubble rise. Once the bubble has cleared at least one meter above everyone's head, ignite the bubble using an extended ignition device.
Disposal	The soap solution can be flushed down the drain with excess water.

Activated Charcoal

Activated charcoal decolorizes and deodorizes many things in our lives.

Application
Organic Chemistry • Consumer Chemistry

Theory
Activated charcoal adsorbs molecules of substances on the surface. Gases, liquids and solids all may be adsorbed. Charcoal is used commercially to remove small amounts of color, odor and other organic molecules such as chloroform from water or remove odors from air. Charcoal is produced from the residue that remains after the destructive distillation of wood. Activated carbon is similar but is prepared in a way that gives it a very large surface area—which increases its reactivity.

Materials
Activated charcoal
Garlic powder
Coffee grounds
Water
Funnel and filter paper
Containers

Safety Precautions
Charcoal is a flammable solid. Wear chemical splash goggles, chemical-resistant gloves and a chemical-resistant apron.

Preparation
Mix 250 mL water, a shake or two of garlic powder and a spoonful of coffee grounds. Shake well.

Demonstration
Pass the sample of water around the room so the color and odor may be noted. Set aside a portion of the water. Add one spoonful of activated charcoal to the water sample and stir or shake vigorously. Set up the funnel and filter paper and filter the sample. Collect the filtrate in a clean container. Pass the filtrate around the room so students can note the changes in color and odor.

Disposal
The solids can be safely discarded in the trash and the solutions flushed down the drain with excess water.

Properties of Gases: Density and Combustion

Igniting balloons filled with different gases will vividly demonstrate the physical and chemical properties of gases.

Application	Gas Properties • Scientific Method • Stoichiometry
Theory	See Demonstration.
Materials	12-in. balloon (5) Hydrogen gas Carbon dioxide gas Helium gas Oxygen gas
Safety Precautions	Wear safety goggles. Use an ignition stick to ignite gases. Have students protect their ears from the explosive sounds. Do not conduct this demonstration in a confined room: Open a window and a door to reduce the concussion of the explosions. Do not use balloons larger than 12 inches. If you plan to repeat this demonstration a number of times, it is advisable to invest in ear protection. The ignition stick may be made by affixing a wooden splint or candle to the end of a meter stick. Never light the balloons directly with a match.
Demonstration	Fill five differently-colored balloons with the following gases: carbon dioxide, oxygen, helium, hydrogen, and a 2:1 mixture of hydrogen and oxygen. Attach a string to each of the balloons and spread them around the front of the demonstration area. Allow at least 1.5 meters between each balloon.
	Begin a discussion of the properties of the unlabeled balloons. Inform the class that each balloon contains a different gas. Have the class review the properties of more familiar gases and develop a method of determining the identity of the gases displayed. Steer the discussion toward the property of flammability of certain gases. Note that certain gases are more dense than air while others are less dense than air. Carbon dioxide is more dense than air and it will not support combustion. Bring the ignition stick toward the carbon dioxide–filled balloon. The balloon should pop and the flame will extinguish. Now repeat the same procedure with each of the balloons. The flame should not go out when testing the oxygen-filled balloon, as oxygen supports combustion. The helium balloon (which floats) also does not support combustion. Note the difference in densities between the hydrogen and helium balloons. The hydrogen is more buoyant, which suggests it is less dense than helium. You may wish to discuss molecular masses of all of these gases. Following the helium balloon, students would be expected to hypothesize that the second to the last balloon contains hydrogen. Note that hydrogen is a very explosive gas. You may wish to bring up the Hindenburg catastrophe (it was filled with hydrogen). Have the students protect their ears. Ignite the hydrogen balloon and expect a large explosive noise (warn your principal ahead of time). Finally, close the lesson by discussing the reactivity of hydrogen, and oxygen as a gas that supports combustion. Ignite the final balloon (hydrogen and oxygen). Expect a phenomenally loud explosion. You may also wish to discuss the 2:1 mixture of these gases.
Disposal	What remains of the balloons may be safely discarded in the trash.

Superconducting — A Levitating Demonstration

To demonstrate superconductivity and the Meissner effect in such a way that the entire class can see.

Application | Physical Properties • Superconductivity • Meissner Effect

Theory | Levitation occurs as the magnet induces a current on the surface of the superconductor. Although normal induction requires movement of a magnet through a coiled wire, this induced current remains even after the magnet stops moving, because the superconductor has no electrical resistance. This "supercurrent", as it is called, in turn induces a magnetic field around the disk. It has just the right field strength and geometry to completely oppose the magnetic field arising from the magnet.

Diamagnetism is the weak repulsion of a material by a magnetic field. It arises from the existence of unpaired electrons in the valence levels of a substance, i.e., O_2. The superconductor is perfectly diamagnetic. Outside of the disk, the field induced by the superconductor and the field caused by the magnet repel each other. This is analogous to the north–north and south–south repulsion in normal bar or disk magnets. The position of the levitated magnet is dictated by the balance between the upward magnetic force of repulsion and the downward gravitational force.

Materials | *Superconductivity and the Meisner Effect,* Flinn demo kit AP1489
    or
High T_c superconductor disk
Rare earth magnet
Liquid nitrogen (see pg. xii)
Plastic forceps
Camcorder and monitor (optional)

Safety Precautions | Use extreme care while handling liquid nitrogen. This extremely cold substance can cause severe frostbite when it contacts the skin. Wearing a pair of leather gloves to protect your skin would be a wise idea. Never store liquid nitrogen in a container with a tight fitting lid. Wash your hands thoroughly after handling the superconductivity disk. Wear chemical splash goggles and always follow laboratory safety rules while performing demonstrations.

Demonstration | Place your superconductor disk on an inverted Styrofoam® cup that has a rim. A TOPS projector, or an overhead projector with a mirror affords an opportunity for the entire class to see the demo. However, the best way to demonstrate with a large group is by monitoring with a camcorder into a large screen TV or monitor.

Pour liquid nitrogen directly on the superconductor and allow a few minutes for its temperature to reach that of the liquid nitrogen (77 K, or –196 °C.)

Using plastic forceps, release a high field strength magnet, (rare earth magnet) over the superconductor and observe the levitation. This is known as the Meissner Effect.

Use a thin wire loop or sheet of paper to demonstrate that the levitation is real! Besides having perfect conductivity, superconductors have perfect diamagnetism. The magnet will remain suspended above the disk until the disk warms to a temperature just above its superconducting critical temperature (T_c). At this point, the magnet may settle to the surface of the disk, or it may jump away from the disk. A thermocouple may be connected to the disk to determine its critical temperature.

The ceramic material of the superconductor is sensitive to moisture, and should be sprayed with a clear lacquer (Krylon no. 1303) to protect it from decomposition. Also, heat it with a heat lamp to remove all moisture after your demonstrations. Store the disk in a dessicator for maximum protection from decomposition due to moisture.

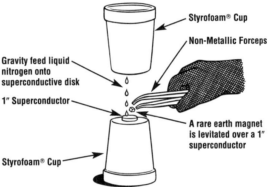

Gravity feed liquid nitrogen onto superconductive disk

1″ Superconductor

Styrofoam® Cup

Styrofoam® Cup

Non-Metallic Forceps

A rare earth magnet is levitated over a 1″ superconductor

Disposal   Allow excess liquid nitrogen to evaporate slowly in its container. One can also dispose of it by pouring it out into a soft patch of soil where it will rapidly vaporize to return to the atmosphere.

Reference   Ellis, A. B. *J. Chem. Ed.* **1987,** *64,* 836–841, 851–853.

CO_2 Extinguisher — Top to Bottom

Hot carbon dioxide is less dense than oxygen and extinguishes candles from the top down.

Application	Gas Properties • Temperature Effects • Density • Combustion
Theory	Candle wax (paraffin wax) combines with oxygen to form carbon dioxide and water. The reactant oxygen is at room temperature. The product carbon dioxide is at a temperature of approximately 275 °C. The density of oxygen at 25 °C is 1.31 g/L and the density of carbon dioxide at 275 °C is 0.978 g/L. Therefore, after burning begins, the oxygen will be located at the bottom of the container because it is denser that the warmer carbon dioxide.
Materials	Candles (3) Cardboard (12 cm × 20 cm) Battery jar, two-liter Hot melt glue gun

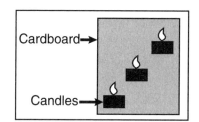

Safety Precautions	Keep flammables away from the open flame. Wear chemical splash goggles and always follow laboratory safety rules while performing demonstrations.
Preparation	Affix the sides of three candles to a piece of cardboard using hot-melt glue. The candles should be staggered horizontally such that no candle will lay directly under another candle. Placing candles on three different height beakers will also work.
Demonstration	Place the cover to be used (battery jar or two-liter beaker) beside the unlighted candles. Ask the students to predict in writing which candle will go out first and to explain why their prediction will occur. After all predictions are completed, light the candles and invert the battery jar (or two-liter beaker) over the assembly. A larger jar will provide more time for all of the candles to extinguish.
Disposal	None required.
Reference	Ruff, Patricia K. "Three Candle Demonstration" in *Demo Den 1992—A Series of Chemical Demonstrations;* Chemistry Teachers' Alliance Group, Millburn, NJ.

CO$_2$ Extinguisher — Bottom to Top

Gaseous carbon dioxide is poured into a vessel containing a number of lit candles, the candles are extinguished one at a time from the bottom up.

Application | Gas Properties • Temperature Effects • Sublimation • Density

Theory | Carbon dioxide (dry ice) sublimes at a temperature of –79 °C. At this temperature, it has a density of 1.56 g/L. The density of oxygen at 25 °C is 1.31 g/L. As the denser gaseous carbon dioxide is poured into a vessel containing a number of lit candles, the candles are extinguished one at a time from the bottom up.

Materials | Candles (6)
Cardboard (30 cm × 50 cm)
Hot melt glue gun
Aquarium, 20-L
Bucket, 10-L
Gloves
Dry ice, CO$_2$(s)

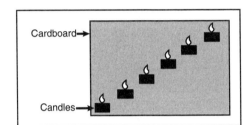

Safety Precautions | Handle dry ice with gloves. Keep flammables away from open flames. Never place dry ice in a sealed container! Wear chemical splash goggles and always follow laboratory safety rules while performing demonstrations.

Preparation | Affix six candles of different heights to a piece of cardboard using hot-melt glue. Place the apparatus upright in an aquarium. Fill a bucket half way with dry ice and allow it to sit undisturbed for about 10 minutes in order to have it fill with CO$_2$(g).

Demonstration | Light the candles and slowly pour the carbon dioxide gas into the aquarium. The candles will extinguish one-by-one from the bottom up.

Disposal | Allow excess dry ice to sublime.

Reference | Alyea, H. N. *J. Chem. Ed.* **1965,** 36.

Separating Metallic Iron from Cereal

Extract metallic iron from dry breakfast cereal.

Application	Metals • Magnetism
Theory	Many cereal companies add fine powdered iron to their cereals as the U.S. RDA for iron. Most people assume that cereals are fortified with a soluble ionic form of iron and not iron in its elemental form. Once ingested, the iron will react with the acid in one's digestive tract to form iron ions which in turn may be absorbed into the body.
Materials	Beaker, 1000-mL Iron fortified cereal (TOTAL®, Product 19®, etc.) Warm water Magnetic stir bar Magnetic stirrer Wash bottle with distilled water Note: Check cereal labels for "reduced iron" or "iron". Some cereals use iron compounds in place of metallic iron.
Safety Precautions	Never eat food in a chemistry lab. Once a food product is brought into a lab it is considered a chemical and not safe for consumption. Wear chemical splash goggles and always follow laboratory safety rules while performing demonstrations.
Preparation	Crush 2 to 3 cups of iron fortified cereal and place in a 1000-mL beaker.
Demonstration	Add enough warm water to fill the beaker containing the cereal to the 750 mL mark. Drop in a large magnetic stir bar and place the beaker on a magnetic stirrer for a few minutes. Remove the bar and rinse carefully with distilled water. This demonstration can also be run in parallel with 2 to 3 different cereals to show differences in iron content. **Alternative procedure:** Shake a plastic bag containing a magnet and a serving of cereal for 1 to 2 minutes. Retrieve the magnet and show black iron on magnet.
Disposal	The solids can be discarded in the trash and the solutions flushed down the drain with excess water.

Ghost Crystals

Show what happens when two substances with almost identical refractive indices are placed together.

Application	Light • Observation • Physical Properties • Polymers
Theory	Polyacrylamide is a super absorbent polymer that is used by gardeners and florists to keep the soil moist around the roots of potted plants. The dehydrated crystals are small (about 1 mm) cubes. When the crystals are placed in water, they absorb approximately 500 times their own mass of water, and grow in size to cubic crystals that are 1 to 2 cm cubes. Since the resulting crystal is almost entirely water, it has a refractive index that is so close to that of water, that it becomes invisible when it is placed into water.
Materials	Polyacrylamide crystals, available from Flinn: G0050 Petri dish Large glass jar with lid Plastic or glass vial with cap Distilled or deionized water
Safety Precautions	Wear chemical splash goggles and always follow laboratory safety rules while performing demonstrations.
Preparation	Place one to two grams of polyacrylamide crystals into a clean one-liter glass jar. Fill the jar with distilled or deionized water. Put the lid on the jar and let stand for a day or two. The crystals will grow and become essentially invisible. Pour out four or five of the crystals into a clean Petri dish. They look like glass but are actually like clear gelatin—very rubbery. Tie a string around one of the crystals, snugly, but not tight enough to cut the crystal in half. Slight compression is all that is necessary. Fill a shell vial with distilled or deionized water, pick up the crystal using the string, and lower it into the vial. The crystal will "disappear". Cap the vial.
Demonstration	Show students the vial with the "empty" noose inside. Let them examine it closely. Ask them if there could be something in the noose that cannot be seen. Uncap the vial and lift out the string to show them the tied-up crystal. Lower it back into the water and let them see how it disappears.
Disposal	Strain out the crystals and mix them with the soil around your potted plants or discard in the trash.
Reference	Robert Becker, Kirkwood High School, Kirkwood, MO.

Is Air Matter?

Most students don't realize that air is matter. This demonstration illustrates that air has mass and takes up space.

Application

Matter • Mass • Volume

Theory

Matter is anything that has mass and takes up space. Examples of matter include a desk, person, rock, etc. Examples of nonmatter include any form of energy: heat, light, sound, etc. Air is matter. It has mass and takes up space.

The volume of a substance can be measured using a technique called water displacement. Since no two objects can occupy the same space at the same time, the water displaced by an object is equal to the volume of the object.

It is important that the mass of the syringe and the mass of the syringe filled with air be taken when the syringe is fully expanded so as to maintain a constant force of buoyancy of air. Buoyancy acts opposite to the downward pull of gravity. Since the mass of air is so small, the buoyancy difference between an expanded and collapsed syringe can be significant.

Materials

50-cc Plastic syringe or bigger (the bigger the better)
Serum cap to seal the syringe
Candle
Nail
Electronic balance, milligram
2-L Graduated cylinder
Cylindrical object, solid (30 cm)
Glass tubing, 1 cm diameter minimum (75 cm)
Balloon, 17″
Large shallow dishpan

Safety Precautions

Wear chemical splash goggles and always follow laboratory safety rules while performing demonstrations.

Preparation

Heat a nail in a burner flame and pass it through the piston of the syringe about 2 cm from the gasket end of the piston.

Demonstration

Fill up a balloon with air. Ask students if the filling of the balloon proves that air has volume. Explain to the students that although a filled balloon looks as if the air displaces matter (an indicator of volume) the matter being displaced is the air surrounding the balloon—not the best choice for an experiment which is supposed to prove that air takes up space.

Completely fill a 2-L graduated cylinder with water. Place the cylinder upside down in a dishpan partially filled with water. Attach the balloon to a tube. Tie the balloon onto the tube if necessary. Blow up the balloon and pinch the end to keep the air in. Place the end of the tube into the graduated cylinder. Release the air from the balloon. The air will quickly fill the cylinder and displace the water.

Place a serum cap over the opening of the syringe. Withdraw the syringe plunger and slide a nail into the hole to keep the plunger from moving into the syringe. There is now a partial vacuum inside the syringe. Determine the mass of the evacuated syringe. Remove the cap and allow the air to be drawn into the syringe. Replace the cap and measure the mass of the syringe filled with air.

You may wish to ask your students to determine a method that will allow one to measure the mass of helium in a balloon.

Disposal None.

Reference Talesnick, I. *The Science Teacher,* **1977,** 44, May.

Chapter 4

Energy

Heat versus Temperature

Students often confuse the terms heat and temperature. Using both of them in the same activity will help to point out the differences between them.

Application | Calorimetry • Heat • Thermochemistry • Thermodynamics

Theory | Heat is a form of energy. Temperature is a quantity proportional to molecular kinetic energy of a system, the coolness or warmness of that system.

The temperature of the system may be determined through the use of a thermometer and measured directly. Heat on the other hand, may only be determined indirectly and compared to a standard value.

The heat content of the system can be determined through the use of the equation:

$$Q = M \cdot c \cdot \Delta T$$

Where Q is heat content of system, M is mass of system, c is heat of system and ΔT is the temperature change of the system.

The specific heat of water is the amount of heat needed to raise the temperature of one gram of water by one degree Celsius (c = 4.18 joules/gram or 1.00 cal/gram).

Materials | Large beaker
Thermometer
Heating method (hot plate or burner and ring stand)
Balance large enough to handle the quantity of water chosen
Graduated cylinder (optional)

Safety Precautions | Wear chemical splash goggles and always follow laboratory safety rules while performing demonstrations.

Demonstration | Measure the temperature of a beaker of "cold" water and record. Heat the water (add energy) noting the temperature rise and final temperature, a rise of about 20 °C is adequate. Call attention to the fact that we now know the temperature of the water and the change in its temperature, ΔT. We do not, however, know how much heat the water contains.

Measure the mass of the water in the beaker. You may choose to measure its volume if you have already considered density. Calculate the heat contained by the water due to the change in temperature using the equation above.

Disposal | None required.

Exothermic Reaction

Many chemical reactions involve energy changes and this exothermic reaction evolves heat as a product.

Application | Thermodynamics • Exothermic • Calorimetry • Heat • Temperature Changes

Theory | When a chemical process releases energy, it is exothermic. The heat is released as chemical bonds are broken and re-formed. If the energy content of the new products is lower than that of the reactants, then the extra energy will be released to the surroundings and may be captured and measured.

Many exothermic reactions are familiar and obvious such as a barbecue fire, the flames on the stove at home or a burning match or lighter. Others are more subtle and less obvious.

Hand warmers are familiar to some students. Heat packs are familiar to others. These are relatively safe reactions to pass around the class. The pocket hand warmer's primary reaction is that of iron with a mixture of sodium chloride and moisture from the air to form iron oxide. The Heat Solution is a re-crystallization of a supersaturated solution of sodium acetate. Some basic measurements of heat may be made by immersing The Heat Solution in a beaker of cold water and measuring the rise in temperature as a side activity to this demonstration.

Materials | Pocket hand warmer, available from Flinn: AP1931
The Heat Solution, available from Flinn: AP1933

Safety Precautions | Both of these are safe to handle although some may find that they do get quite hot. Warn students of this. Devices may be wrapped in a towel if too hot. Do not open either of these devices. Wear chemical splash goggles and always follow laboratory safety rules while performing demonstrations.

Demonstration | Pass the packet among the students to determine that it is room temperature. Initiate the reaction after explaining why the demo is being done. Re-circulate the packet among the students so they may convince themselves that this is indeed exothermic. Capture the heat, but only use the heat solution for this optional activity.

Point out that even the rusting of nails, though much slower, produces the same amount of heat.

Disposal | The pocket hand warmer may be safely discarded in the trash. The Heat Solution may be saved and re-used many times and then safely discarded in the trash.

Reference | Chemfax No. 1933, Flinn Scientific, Inc., Batavia, IL, 1990.

Flameless Heater

Construct and demonstrate the reaction of a Flameless Ration Heater.

Application | Exothermic Reactions • Consumer Chemistry • Redox

Theory | The Flameless Ration Heater (FRH) contains magnesium metal which, when mixed with water, forms magnesium hydroxide and heat:

$$Mg + 2H_2O \rightarrow Mg(OH)_2 + H_2 + Heat$$

Each mole of magnesium metal releases 355 kJ of energy. This is enough energy to boil one liter of water. The FRH is an effective devise for camping or Army use as it produces a large amount of heat without flame or smoke.

Since magnesium has a natural protective coating of magnesium oxide, MgO, which inhibits spontaneous reaction with water. Sodium chloride, NaCl, is added, along with powdered iron to increase the rate of reaction between the water and the magnesium. Chloride ions react with the magnesium hydroxide to form Mg(OH)Cl which increases the solubility of the oxide coating, thus exposing more of the magnesium metal. The iron powder acts as a catalyst to transfer hydrogen atoms from the water to the magnesium.

Materials | *Flameless Ration Heater,* Flinn demo kit AP8695
 or
Magnesium ribbon (10 cm)
Sharp knife
Iron powder
Anvil or similar sturdy metal surface
Hammer
18×150 mm Test tube
Table salt, NaCl
Water
Thermometer

Safety Precautions | Magnesium is a flammable solid; burns with an intense flame: Iron powder also presents a serious fire and explosion risk. Keep either dry sand or Flinn Met-L-X® available to use as a fire extinguisher. Wear chemical splash goggles, chemical-resistant gloves and a chemical-resistant apron.

Preparation | Remove the oxide coating from the magnesium ribbon by scraping both sides with a sharp knife. Sprinkle some iron powder over the surface of the anvil. Lay the ribbon on the coated anvil and sprinkle iron powder over the surface of the magnesium. Hammer the ribbon to imbed the iron into the surface of the magnesium ribbon.

Demonstration	Coil the magnesium ribbon and place it at the bottom of the test tube. Place a few crystals of salt in with the magnesium. Pour about 1 to 2 mL of water into the test tube. Hydrogen bubbles should form on the surface of the magnesium. As the reaction takes place the test tube will slowly heat up. Note: The gas can be collected and tested for the presence of hydrogen gas using a flaming wooden splint.

The U.S. Army Natick Research, Development and Engineering Center jointly developed the FRH with Zesto Therm of Cincinnati, OH. The FRH is now standard Army issue for soldiers in the field. |
| **Disposal** | All materials can be safely discarded in the trash or flushed down the drain with excess water. |
| **References** | Scott, D. *Chem Matters,* American Chemical Society, 1992.
Chemfax No. 10074, Flinn Scientific, Inc., Batavia, IL, 1993. |

Chemiluminescence — The Firefly Reaction

An exothermic reaction in which the energy released is in the form of light.

Application | Exothermic • Chemiluminescence • Energy

Theory | Exothermic reactions yields energy. This energy is usually in the form of heat. Sometimes, both light and heat are emitted. Chemiluminescent reactions yield primarily light energy, with little or no heat. Fireflies produce their flashes with chemiluminescent reactions.

Materials

500-mL Flask	Sodium carbonate, Na_2CO_3
2-L Erlenmeyer flask	Sodium bicarbonate, $NaHCO_3$
Tygon tubing (1 m)	Luminol, 3-aminophthalhydrazide
Ring stand	Cupric sulfate pentahydrate, $CuSO_4 \cdot 5H_2O$
Tape	3% Hydrogen peroxide solution, H_2O_2
Plastic funnel	Ammonium Carbonate, $(NH_4)_2CO_3 \cdot H_2O$

Safety Precautions | A 3% solution of hydrogen peroxide is very weak but it is still an oxidizer and a skin and eye irritant. Wear chemical splash goggles, chemical-resistant gloves and a chemical-resistant apron.

Preparation | Prepare the following solutions:

Solution A: In a 500-mL flask, dissolve 2.0 g of sodium carbonate in approximately 300 mL of distilled water. Add 0.1 g of luminol, stir to dissolve. Add 12.0 g of sodium bicarbonate, 0.25 g of ammonium carbonate monohydrate and 0.2 g of cupric sulfate pentahydrate, stir to form a solution. Dilute to 500 mL.

Solution B: In a 500-mL flask, add 25 mL of 3% hydrogen peroxide, dilute to 500 mL and mix well. Prepare this solution within an hour of performing the demonstration.

Prepare a spiral of Tygon tubing (from your hardware store or scientific supplier) and tape around a ring stand. Affix a funnel to the top end of the tubing and clamp securely to the stand. The lower end of the tubing enters a 2-L collection flask.

Demonstration | To perform this demonstration, dim the lights and slowly pour the contents of both flasks simultaneously into the funnel. The solutions will react and release a blue glow.

Disposal | The solution can be flushed down the drain with excess water.

Reference | Summerlin, L. *Chemical Demonstration;* American Chemical Society: Washington, DC, 1988; Vol. 1, p 71.

Chemical Cold Pack — An Endothermic Process

Ammonium nitrate is mixed with water producing a spontaneous endothermic reaction.

Application	Endothermic Reactions • Heat • Enthalpy
Theory	An endothermic reaction is one in which the chemical change absorbs energy. In these reactions the energy content of the products is greater than the energy content of the reactants.

When ammonium nitrate dissolves in water the reaction is:

$$NH_4NO_3(s) + 26.2 \text{ kJ/mol} \rightarrow NH_4^+(aq) + NO_3^-(aq)$$

You can expect a drop in temperature of approximately 20 °C when equal volumes of ammonium nitrate and water are mixed.

Cold packs which are used in first aid kits or by athletes usually contain about 200 grams ammonium nitrate sealed in a pouch. Within this pouch is found yet another, but smaller pouch containing water. To activate the cold pack, one needs to squeeze the pack in order to rupture the inner pouch of water, which in turn mixes with the ammonium nitrate. It is worthwhile purchasing a cold pack and opening it for students to see that chemistry is everywhere.

Materials

Ammonium nitrate or ammonium chloride, NH_4NO_3 or NH_4Cl (10 g)
Large test tube
Rubber stopper, one-hole
Thermometer
Cold pack (available at drug stores)

Safety Precautions

Ammonium nitrate is a strong oxidizing agent in dry form. Keep away from flammable materials. Wear chemical splash goggles, chemical-resistant gloves and a chemical-resistant apron.

Demonstration

Insert a thermometer into a one-hole rubber stopper. Fill a large test tube half full of water. Measure and record the temperature of the water in the test tube. Add approximately 10 g ammonium nitrate to the water, affix the stopper with the thermometer in place and mix for ten seconds. Measure the change in temperature. Continue mixing until the coldest attainable temperature is reached.

Disposal

All solutions can be flushed down the drain with excess water.

Photochemical Bleaching of Thionin

To show that light instead of heat can initiate a chemical reaction.

Application	Activation Energy • Redox
Theory	Thionin, a blue biological dye related to methylene blue, is an oxidizing agent. When the dye molecule absorbs visible light, it becomes a stronger oxidizing agent and is capable of oxidizing Fe^{2+} to Fe^{3+}.

The reaction can be represented by:

$$Thio^+ + 2\,Fe^{2+} + 2\,H^+ \rightarrow ThioH^{2+} + 2\,Fe^{3+}$$
(purple)   (colorless)

$Thio^+$ represents the monoprotonated or oxidized form of the dye. $ThioH^{2+}$ represents the triprotonated or reduced form. The above solution will maintain its photosensitivity indefinitely, provided that the container is sealed tightly against atmospheric oxygen. Oxygen oxidizes iron(II) to iron(III), and when iron(II) is not available, the solution will no longer bleach upon exposure to light.

Materials	Ferrous sulfate, 4% solution, $FeSO_4$	600-mL Beaker
	Sulfuric acid, 3 M, H_2SO_4	1-L Beaker or jar
	Thionin solution	Overhead projector

Safety Precautions	Sulfuric acid is toxic and severely corrosive to eyes, skin and other tissue. Use extreme caution when handling. Considerable heat of dilution with water. Always add the acid to the water, never the reverse. Ferrous sulfate is toxic. Wear chemical splash goggles, chemical-resistant gloves, and a chemical-resistant apron.
Preparation	Prepare thionin solution (0.03 g in 100 mL distilled water) and $FeSO_4$ solution (2 g in 50 mL distilled water). Place 250 mL of distilled water in a 600-mL beaker. Add 50 mL of the $FeSO_4$ solution, 10 mL of 3 M H_2SO_4, and 10 mL of the thionin solution. Dilute this mixture to 500 mL with distilled water and transfer it to the 2-L beaker or jar.
Demonstration	Shine a spot of bright light on the purple solution. Where the light strikes the solution, it will first turn magenta, and then colorless. When the light is removed, the color will return. Placing the flask on an overhead projector also works well.
	To illustrate that light rather than heat is responsible for the color change, place aluminum foil under half of the container so that only half of the solution is exposed to light. Only the part of the solution exposed to light will turn colorless.
Disposal	The two-faced solution may be rinsed down the drain with excess water.
References	Woodrow Wilson Chem 4 Institute.
	Robert J. Cairo, Horace Mann School, Bronx, NY.

Chapter 5

Atomic Theory

Think Tube — An Analogous Model

To illustrate that all atomic models are based on indirect evidence.

Application | Models • Atomic Theory • Scientific Method

Theory | The atomic theory is based on the collaborative efforts and indirect observations made by many scientists that explain the composition of atoms. A tube with four protruding strings is manipulated in such a way to provoke interest in the tube's construction. Without opening the tube, its construction may be determined through indirect observations.

Materials | Mail tube or PVC pipe with end caps, 60-cm length
Washers (5)
Strings (nylon works best), 60-cm (2)
Awl or nail

Safety Precautions | Wear chemical splash goggles and always follow laboratory safety rules while performing demonstrations.

Preparation | Construct the tube as indicated below. Glue the end caps to prevent the tube from being opened. One string is attached to washer 1, enters tube and passes through washer 5, and then back out of the tube to be connected to washer 3. Holes must be 180° apart.

The other string is attatched to washer 2, enters tube and passes through washer 5, and then back out to washer 4.

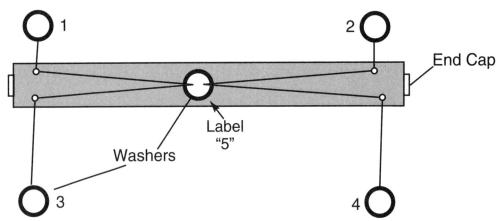

Demonstration | Hold the tube so that the bottom two strings (3 and 4) are fully extended and hanging as indicated in the diagram. While inconspicuously pinching string 3 at the base of the tube, pull up on string 2. Pull string 4 to return the tube to its original configuration. Now do the same to the other side of the tube: While pinching string 4 at the base of the tube, pull up on string 1 and return the strings to the original configuration.

Instruct students to draw in their notebooks how they think the tube is constructed.

While pinching string 3, pull up on string 1. String 4 should move up. Return the string to the original configuration. While pinching string 4, pull up on string 2. String 3 should move up. Return the string to the original configuration.

Instruct students to revise their models of the tube based on what they have just learned.

Pull on string 1 without pinching any strings. Strings 2, 3 and 4 should all be pulled into the tube.

Have students propose their own explanations as to the construction of the think tube. You may wish to have your students construct their own tubes at home.

Note: Do not open the tube and present the contents to your students. Remember, this is to serve as a model which is analogous to the atomic model. Scientists can't open up atoms to see if "they are right".

Disposal   None required.

Reference   Robert Lewis, Downers Grove High School, Downers Grove, IL, Woodrow Wilson Chem 5 Institute.

Flame Tests

A variation of the common flame test.

Application	Flame Tests • Atomic Theory • Spectroscopy
Theory	When atoms are excited due to an increase in energy, electrons absorb this extra energy and are forced into higher energy levels. An atom in an excited state is unstable since the lower levels, as a result, do not have complete configurations. In turn, electrons must move down to these lower levels to fill in the voids. In order to accomplish this, electrons must give off the "gained energy". The release of this energy is commonly in the form of light. The characteristics of this light are unique for most elements. One may observe the light in order to make out its spectrum. Such a technique, called spectroscopy, can be used to identify unknown elements. This particular method is more convenient than the traditional platinum loop method as it produces a large, longer lasting flame which may be readily observed.

The following substances emit these colors during the flame tests:

Lithium chloride: red	Strontium chloride: scarlet
Sodium chloride: yellow	Barium chloride: yellow-green
Potassium chloride: violet	Cupric chloride: blue-green
Calcium chloride: orange-red	Cesium chloride: deep violet

Materials	*Flame Test/Emmission Spectroscopy Kit,* Flinn demo kit AP1716 　　or 400-mL Beaker Pyrex® watch glasses, Petri dishes or porcelain evaporating dishes Aqueous metal chloride solutions (LiCl, NaCl, KCl, CuCl, etc.) Methanol, CH_3OH or ethanol, C_2H_5OH Wooden splints Optional: spray bottles (mist type) 　　　　Q-Tips®
Safety Precautions	Keep flammable materials away from open flames. Use a large beaker as a cover to extinguish a flaming watch glass. Wear chemical splash goggles, chemical-resistant gloves and a chemical-resistant apron.
Demonstration	A few drops of various metal chloride solutions are placed separately into a lineup of watch glasses (Petri dishes also work well). The watch glasses are then topped off with methanol which will form a solution with the aqueous metal chlorides. The solutions are then ignited with a wooden splint resulting in a flame of characteristic color. This method is useful in comparing colors that appear to be similar: for example, Li and Sr. Extinguish the flame by covering the watch glasses with an inverted 400-mL beaker. Be careful not to overheat the watch glasses—they sometimes crack. Glass furniture coasters work well in place of watch glasses.

Alternate Demonstration

Procedure A: Soak wood splints in distilled or deionized water for several hours. Place solid metal chlorides in spot plates, dip water-soaked splints into samples of solids. Hold splints in the flame, observe. Only a few crystals of solid are needed on the damp splint.

Procedure B: Place solutions of metallic chlorides in spray bottles. Spray solutions into the flame of a Bunsen burner.

Procedure C: Dip one end of a cotton swab (Q-Tip®) into a solution of the metallic chloride and and hold in the flame.

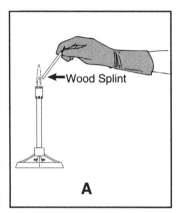
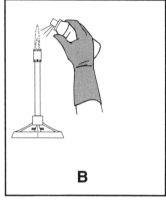
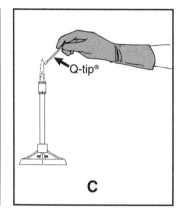

Disposal

The solids (except barium chloride) can be discarded in the trash and the solutions flushed down the drain with excess water. Barium chloride can be disposed of by Flinn Suggested Disposal Method #27h.

Reference

Sue Zoltewicz, Eastside High School, Gainesville, FL, and Otto Phanstiell, Episcopal High School, Jacksonville, FL, at the 1984 Dreyfus Summer Workshop.

Mass Spectrometer

This demonstration simulates the operation of a mass spectrometer and separating atoms of different atomic mass.

Application | Spectroscopy • Atomic Mass • Isotopes

Theory | Invented by Nobel Laureate F. W. Aston, an English physicist, the mass spectrometer is one of the most versatile instruments used in a chemistry laboratory. The mass spectrometer separates mixtures of atoms by their atomic masses. A mass spectrometer functions by first ionizing a vaporized sample by bombarding it with a beam of electrons. The electron beam causes the atoms within the sample to lose electrons leaving these atoms with a positive charge. This vapor of charged atoms is then accelerated as a narrow beam of particles through a magnetic and electric field. As the atoms pass through the electric and magnetic fields they are deflected because of their charge. The amount of deflection depends upon the mass of the individual atoms. Thus a mixture of atoms of various masses can be sorted according to their mass. Aston used this technique to prove that many samples of naturally occurring elements were in fact mixtures of isotopes.

Steel spheres of various diameters and masses are used to represent the different isotopes of an element. Students may also observe the effects of accelerating these "particles". Particles of lighter mass will be deflected more in the magnetic field than particles of heavier mass, provided their charges are equal and the velocity with which they enter the magnetic field is identical. The "ions" or "atoms" are collected on the sides of the Plexiglas® plate in their respective "detectors" consisting of channels created with Popsicle® sticks glued to a plastic sheet.

Materials | *Mass Spectrometer Model Kit,* Flinn demo kit AP8717
    or
Magnet (strong)
Metal picture frame, 50 × 100 cm
Plexiglas, 50 × 100 cm
Popsicle sticks (9)
Hot melt glue
Slotted inclined plane
Steel spheres of various masses
Plastic spheres
Blocks of wood (4)

Safety Precautions | Wear chemical splash goggles and always follow laboratory safety rules while performing demonstrations.

Preparation

The simulated mass spectrometer is constructed to look like the diagram below. Replace the glass pane of a picture frame with a sheet of thin Plexiglas. The back of the frame will serve as the top surface of the mass spectrometer such that the frame itself will serve to contain the rolling spheres. Glue seven Popsicle sticks at one end of the frame to create eight collection boxes for spheres. The Popsicle sticks should be laid to create channels into which the spheres will roll. A magnet is placed under the Plexiglas. The strength of the magnet and the mass of spheres used should dictate the position of the launching pad in respect to the magnet. Practice!

Demonstration

Launch the various spheres down the grooved ramp, one at a time. The ramp may be held in place using tape. To show the necessity of ionizing the atoms, a sphere of non-metallic material may be sent down the launcher as well (this sphere will be unaffected by the magnet). It is important that the path of the launched sphere cross the magnetic field at the two ends of the magnet.

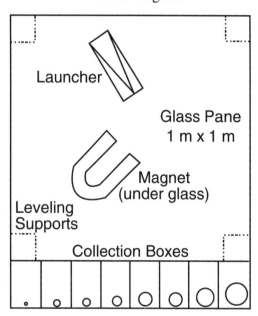

Disposal

None required.

Reference

Eberhardt, W. H. *J. Chem. Ed.* **1946,** *23,* 220.

Telesnick, I. *Idea Bank Book;* S17 Science Supplies and Services: Thornhill, Canada, 1984; p 51.

Emission and Absorption Spectra

Emission and absorption spectra can be observed by an entire class using diffraction grating.

Application   Spectroscopy • Emission Spectra • Atomic Theory

Theory   Rainbow glasses or Flinn C-Spectra® contain excellent diffraction grating replicas that yield very good spectra. The rare earth element solutions produce absorption spectra with relatively fine lines.

Materials   *Absorption Spectroscopy Kit*, Flinn demo kit AP8823
        or
Erbium chloride, praseodymium chloride or yttrium chloride
Gas discharge tubes, helium and neon
Rainbow glasses (Flinn, AP1949)
Flinn C-Spectra® (Flinn, AP1714)
Incandescent aquarium light and socket
Excitation source for gas discharge tubes
Test tube, 10×75 or 13×100 mm

Safety Precautions   Wear chemical splash goggles and always follow laboratory safety rules while performing demonstrations.

Preparation   Dissolve 1 to 2 grams of the rare earth chloride in as small an amount of distilled or deionized water as possible. Put this solution in a small test tube.

Demonstration   Distribute the Rainbow glasses or Flinn C-Spectra® to the students. Set up the gas discharge tube and turn on. Allow students to observe the emission spectra of the gases. Give them time to write down their observations. Have them sketch what they see.

Turn on the aquarium light and position the test tube in front of it, so that students see the light after it passes through the solution. Have them observe through the rainbow glasses, and sketch what they see.

Disposal   None required. Keep the solutions in the test tube for further use.

References   John Brodemus, H. L. Richards High School, Oaklawn, IL.
Carolyn Morse, Chapel Hill High School, Chapel Hill, NC.
Norma McKenzie, Charlotte Country Day School, Charlotte, NC.

Colored H₂ Balloon Explosions

A dramatic variation of flame tests uses exploding balloons.

Application | Flame Tests • Atomic Theory • Spectroscopy • Explosions

Theory | When atoms are excited due to an increase in energy, electrons absorb this extra energy and are forced into higher energy levels. An atom in an excited state is unstable since the lower energy levels, as a result, do not have complete configurations. In turn, electrons must move down to these lower levels to fill in the voids. In order to accomplish this, electrons must give off the "gained energy". The release of this energy is commonly in the form of light. The characteristics of this light are unique for most elements. One may observe the light in order to make out its spectrum. Such a technique, called spectroscopy, can be used to identify unknown elements.

Materials | Hydrogen gas cylinder
Balloons, 14 inch round
String
Solids, e.g., strontium nitrate, cupric chloride, potassium chloride, cesium chloride powdered iron
Ignition source—tape a candle to a meter stick

Safety Precautions | Wear chemical splash goggles when inflating the balloons with hydrogen and when igniting the balloons. If a balloon were to pop, solid particles would be thrust out in all directions.

In smaller rooms, reduce the amount of the solid. To ensure combustion of the solid, avoid igniting the balloon above the stem area. Instruct the audience to cover their ears and to wear chemical splash goggles. The demonstration is excellent if done outside or in large gymnasium or auditorium. Do not use toxic salts such as barium, lithium, etc. Do not use aluminum powder, as the reactions will result in the formation of $Al(OH)_3$, which irritates the lungs and throat. Check hazard alert before choosing individual salts.

Preparation | This is a dramatic variation on ways to demonstrate flame tests. Simply add about a teaspoon of the solid to a balloon and then inflate the balloon with hydrogen to a diameter of about 20 cm. Tie a string to the balloon and anchor it. The solid will settle to the bottom of the floating balloon around the stem.

Demonstration | The candle flame is brought up to that point and the resulting explosion will take on the color of the flame test. Cupric chloride gives a nice blue, strontium nitrate produces a bright red, iron powder gives a yellow sparkle. Other salts can produce a rainbow of colors, but avoid salts of toxic metals.

Disposal | If pieces of the balloons are found, they can be discarded in the trash.

Reference | Fortman, J. J. *J. Chem. Ed.* **1991,** *68,* 168.

Chapter 6

Chemical Reactions

Evidence of a Chemical Change

Many chemical changes provide evidence that is easily observed and identified.

Application   Chemical Reactions • Chemical Properties • Precipitation

Theory   Chemical reactions may be detected by the production of heat, light, sound, loss of heat, color change, formation of a precipitate, or the formation of a new substance (solid, liquid, or gas). Most students can relate to the first few of these, however the others are generally less familiar to them.

When two or more substances react, concrete evidence of reaction is often obvious. Some less common evidence types will be explored here.

Materials   Specific materials used will vary, but some examples are given.
Silver nitrate and sodium chloride solutions, 0.01–0.1 M, $AgNO_3$ and NaCl
Liquid latex and vinegar
Lead nitrate and potassium iodide solutions, 0.01–0.1 M, $PbNO_3$ and KI
Sodium hydroxide and hydrochloric acid solutions, 3 M, NaOH and HCl
250-mL Erlenmeyer flasks

Safety Precautions   Specific precautions will be dependent upon the particular reactions that are used, please check the *Flinn Chemical Catalog/Reference Manual*. Wear chemical splash goggles, chemical-resistant gloves and a chemical-resistant apron.

Preparation   Set up Erlenmeyer flasks with one of the substances in the flask, about 25 mL. Place a 13×100 mm test tube half filled with the other reactant, on a slant inside the flask. Stopper each flask tightly, taking care to not mix the reactants.

Demonstration   Note the physical properties of the two substances in one of the flasks. Tip the flask so that the contents mix. Call attention to the change(s) that occur. Tip another flask. Repeat the observations. Involve students by having them tip the flasks and record observations on the board. Ask them to predict what might happen. Depending upon how the demo is applied, define terms, write equations, identify materials, etc. as a follow-up.

Disposal   Specific disposal methods will be chosen based upon the reactions run. Consult the procedures for disposal in your *Flinn Chemical Catalog/Reference Manual*.

Electrolysis of Potassium Iodide

To demonstrate the action when an aqueous solution of potassium iodide is electrolyzed.

Application	Redox • Electrolysis
Theory	A 9-volt battery makes a good power supply for this electrolysis. The reactions are as follows:

Cathode reaction: $2H_2O + 2e^- \rightarrow + 2\ OH^-(aq) + H_2(g)$

Anode reaction: $2\ I^-(aq) \rightarrow I_2(g) + 2e^-$

The hydroxide ion in the solution around the cathode will cause a pink color if phenolphthalein is added, and the iodine at the anode will react with starch.

Materials	U-tube 9-volt Battery and cap with wires Potassium iodide, 0.5 M, KI Phenolphthalein indicator solution Starch solution (spray starch or liquid laundry starch works well!!) Dropper pipet (2)
Safety Precautions	Wear chemical splash goggles, chemical-resistant gloves and a chemical-resistant apron.
Preparation	Prepare potassium iodide (8.3 g KI in 100 mL H_2O) and starch solutions. Make sure that about 1 cm of insulation is stripped off the ends of the wires from the battery cap. Attach the cap to the battery, do not allow the bare wire ends to touch.
Demonstration	Fill the U-tube with the potassium iodide solution. Put a drop or two of phenol-phthalein into both sides of the U-tube. Insert the wires from the battery cap into different sides of the U-tube, making sure that they are both immersed. Have students observe and record what they see. After a few minutes, put a drop or two of the starch solution into each side of the U-tube. Again have students observe and record their observations. Ask them which wire acts as the cathode and which as the anode. This demo can easily be done as a micro-scale lab, using regular glass tubing bent into a "mini" U-tube.
Disposal	Disconnect the cap from the battery. Rinse and dry the wires that were immersed in the solution. The solution can be flushed down the drain with excess water.
Reference	Kolb, K. E.; Kolb, D. K. *J. Chem. Ed.* **1987,** *64,* 891, and **1986,** *63,* 517.

Micro-Generation of Chlorine and Acetylene

Demonstrate the reaction between chlorine gas and acetylene gas.

Application

Exothermic • Gaseous Reactions

Theory

The reactions are:

Acetylene generation:
$$CaC_2(s) + 2\,H_2O(l) \rightarrow C_2H_2(g) + Ca(OH)_2(aq)$$

Chlorine generation:
$$2\,KMnO_4 + 16\,HCl \rightarrow 2\,KCl + 2\,MnCl_2 + 5\,Cl_2 + 8H_2O$$

Acetylene/chlorine:
$$C_2H_2(g) + Cl_2(g) \rightarrow C(s) + 2HCl(aq) + C_2H_2Cl_2 + heat + light$$

The reaction of the acetylene with chlorine is a mixture of reduction and addition reactions. In the reduction reaction, chlorine removes the hydrogen atoms from the acetylene, forming HCl and carbon. The carbon product is visible as soot. Chlorine also adds to acetylene to produce chlorinated hydrocarbons such as dichloro-ethylene. Both are very exothermic reaction, with both light and heat being produced. The quantities are kept small by the apparatus design, and the heat produced is easily absorbed by the water in the hydrometer jar.

Materials

Underwater Fireworks, Flinn demo kit AP8728
   or
13×100 mm Test tube
Stopper, 2-hole #00
Beral-type pipet, thin stem
Gas delivery tube with jet tip
Potassium permanganate, $KMnO_4$
Hydrochloric acid, 12 M, HCl
Hydrometer cylinder or large (500-mL) graduated cylinder
Calcium carbide, CaC_2

Safety Precautions

Potassium permanganate is a powerful oxidizing agent; can explode on sudden heating strong skin irritant reacts with acid to evolve chlorine gas; evolves chlorine when heated; toxic by ingestion; avoid contact with organic material.

Hydrochloric acid is highly toxic by ingestion or inhalation; severely corrosive to skin and eyes. Calcium carbide is corrosive to eyes and skin; exposure to water or moisture evolves flammable acetylene gas. We urge you to have adequate ventilation when doing this demonstration. Wear chemical splash goggles, chemical-resistant gloves, and a chemical-resistant apron.

Preparation

Insert the delivery tube and the thin stem Beral-type pipet into the rubber stopper. Place about one gram of potassium permanganate crystals in the test tube.

Demonstration Fill the hydrometer jar nearly full with water. Fill the Beral-type pipet with the concentrated HCl. Insert the stopper assembly into the test tube and place the delivery tube into the hydrometer jar. Add a small amount of calcium carbide to the water in the hydrometer jar to begin generation of the acetylene. Squeeze a small amount of the conc. HCl from the Beral-type pipet so that it mixes with the permanganate in the test tube, this will begin generation of the chlorine. When bubbles of chlorine contact bubbles of acetylene, they react spontaneously, emitting a flash of light.

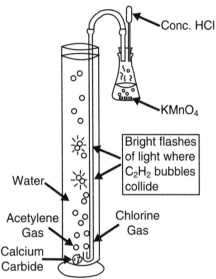

Conc. HCl

KMnO₄

Bright flashes of light where C₂H₂ bubbles collide

Water

Acetylene Gas

Chlorine Gas

Calcium Carbide

Disposal Allow the calcium carbide to react completely before disposing of the solution, which can be rinsed down the drain with excess water.

References Walter Rohr, Eastchester High School, Eastchester, NY.

Chemfax No. 10081, Flinn Scientific, Inc, Batavia, IL.

Shakashiri, B. Z. *Chemical Demonstrations;* University of Wisconsin: Madison, WI, 1988; Vol. 2, p 227.

Dehydrating Sucrose

Table sugar is decomposed by sulfuric acid to produce a visible cloud of steam and a solid mass of carbon that rises out of a beaker.

Application | Organic Chemistry • Hygroscopic • Chemical Reaction • Exothermic

Theory | The hygroscopic nature of sulfuric acid extracts the water from the carbohydrate structure of the sucrose leaving the less reactive carbon behind. The heat of reaction causes the water in the solution to turn into steam (water vapor).

$$C_{12}H_{22}O_{11} \rightarrow 12C + 11H_2O + heat$$

Materials | *The Carbon Souffle,* Flinn demo kit AP4422
   or
50-mL Beaker
Sucrose or table sugar (10–15 g)
Water (1 mL)
Sulfuric acid, 18 M, H_2SO_4 (10 mL)
Stirring rod

Safety Precautions | Sulfuric acid is severely corrosive to eyes, skin and other tissue; extremely hazardous in contact with finely divided materials, carbides, chlorates, nitrates and other combustible materials. Wear a chemical-resistant apron, chemical-resistant gloves and a chemical splash face shield.

Do not handle the carbon product; use tongs. The carbon product will contain unreacted sulfuric acid. Neutralize acid spills and the carbon product with sodium carbonate.

The steam produced by the reaction can cause burns. Do not stand over the reaction vessel or inhale the steam produced. The reaction vessel will get extremely hot; allow the vessel to cool before handling. Perform this demonstration only in an efficient fume hood or a well-ventilated room.

Demonstration | Place 10 g sucrose in a 50-mL beaker. Add 1 mL water and stir. Pour 10 mL concentrated sulfuric acid onto the sugar mixture; stir briskly. Step back and watch.

Disposal | When the reaction is complete and the reaction vessel is cool, remove the carbon product from the reaction vessel by the use of tongs, and sprinkle the carbon product with sodium carbonate to help neutralize the remaining acid. Thoroughly rinse the carbon product under running water. Place the carbon lump inside a plastic bag. Seal the bag then place it in the trash.

References | Shakhashiri, B. Z. *Chemical Demonstrations: A Handbook for Teachers of Chemistry;* Vol. 1; The University of Wisconsin: Madison, WI, 1983.

Summerlin, L. R. and Ealy, J. L. Jr. *Chemical Demonstrations: A Sourcebook for Teachers,* Vol. 1; American Chemical Society: Washington, DC, 1988.

Elephant Toothpaste

Catalytic decomposition of hydrogen peroxide rapidly releases oxygen gas, producing a large quantity of foam.

Application | Catalyst • Exothermic

Theory | Hydrogen peroxide typically decomposes at a rate of approximately 10% per year, producing water and oxygen gas. The rate of this reaction can be increased by introducing a catalyst—in this case potassium iodide will serve as the catalyst. Powdered manganese dioxide or the manganese dioxide coating on manganese chips will also catalyze the decomposition of hydrogen peroxide.

Materials | *Old Foamy,* Flinn demo kit AP2085   Wooden splint
or   Water
250-mL Graduated cylinder   Dishpan
Liquid dishwashing
    detergent (5 mL)
Potassium iodide, KI (10 g)
Hydrogen peroxide, 30% solution, H_2O_2 (50 mL)

Safety Precautions | 30% Hydrogen peroxide will act as an oxidizing agent with practically any substance. It deserves the science teacher's special handling and storage attention. This substance is severely corrosive to the skin, eyes and respiratory tract; a very strong oxidant; and a dangerous fire and explosion risk. Do not heat this substance. Sodium iodide is moderately toxic. Do not stand over the reaction; steam and oxygen are produced quickly. Wear chemical splash goggles, chemical-resistant gloves and chemical-resistant apron.

Preparation | Prepare a dishwashing detergent/potassium iodide solution by first dissolving 10 grams potassium iodide in 5 mL water. Add this solution to 25 mL liquid dishwashing detergent. Place a 250-mL graduated cylinder in a large shallow dishpan. Add the soap mixture to the graduate cylinder.

Demonstration | Quickly pour 50 mL hydrogen peroxide into the graduated cylinder. Use caution! A foam-like snake should quickly push out of the graduate cylinder and spill into the dishpan. This is an exothermic reaction and a tremendous amount of steam may be produced.

As the foam is produced, insert a burning wooden splint into the foam. The splint will continue to burn due to the presence of oxygen.

Disposal | The foam and solution left in the cylinder may be rinsed down the drain with excess water.

Reference | Stone, C. H. *J. Chem. Ed.* **1944,** *21,* 300.
Jim and Julie Ealy, The Peddie School, Hightstown, NJ.

Reaction of Magnesium with Dry Ice

Magnesium reacts with dry ice to produce a brilliant flame.

Application Combustion • Metals

Theory Carbon dioxide will react with magnesium. This presents a problem to firefighters involved in putting out fires involving magnesium and similar metals. A magnesium fire is nearly impossible to extinguish. In air, the reaction is:

$$2Mg + O_2 \rightarrow 2MgO$$

When magnesium reacts with hot water or steam, the reaction is:

$$Mg + 2H_2O \rightarrow Mg(OH)_2 + H_2$$

When reacting with CO_2, the reaction is:

$$2Mg + CO_2 \rightarrow 2MgO + C$$

Magnesium will also react with SiO_2 in the same manner as with CO_2.

Materials Dry ice blocks, $12 \times 12 \times 7$ cm (2)
Magnesium turnings
Ball peen hammer
Large fire-resistant surface
Bunsen burner or propane torch
Gloves
Safety shield

Safety Precautions Dry ice can cause frostbite. Magnesium is a flammable solid that burns with an intense flame.

Remove all combustible items from the area before burning the magnesium in dry ice, and work on a noncombustible surface.

Caution the students not to look directly at the magnesium burning in air since ultraviolet radiation is produced. Wear dark colored welder glasses, noncombustible insulated gloves, and a chemical-resistant apron.

Preparation Two blocks of dry ice are needed, with a minimum size of $12 \times 12 \times 7$ cm, with one set of large smooth surfaces. The depth of the block is somewhat critical since the magnesium could burn through a thinner block. In one block, a rough cavity about 2 to 3 cm deep and about 4 cm in diameter should be scooped out. A large cork borer works well for this purpose. Heating the round end of a ball peen hammer will also provide a method to "melt" a hole in the surface of the dry ice.

Fill the cavity with magnesium turnings and place the dry ice on a fire resistant surface behind an explosion shield.

Demonstration	Ignite the magnesium by heating it from above with a Bunsen burner flame. Using a 5 cm piece of magnesium ribbon as a fuse helps. Once the metal is ignited, place the second block of dry ice over the burning magnesium. The intense light easily penetrates the block of ice. Darken the room to enhance the effect. After the reaction is completed, the products can be exposed to view.
Disposal	The products of the reaction can be dissolved in water and washed down the drain with excess water. Allow excess dry ice to sublime in a well ventilated room.
Reference	Chemfax No. 468, Flinn Scientific, Batavia, IL, 1990.

Gun Cotton

This historically significant chemistry will disappear before your student's eyes!

Application | Combustion • Organic Chemistry

Theory | Dehydration of the cellulose in cotton and subsequent nitration produces cellulose nitrate, gun cotton. The combustion is rapid and produces almost no ash due to the nitrate oxidizing agent. This is historically significant since many films were once made from cellulose nitrates.

The combustion is smokeless since only gases are produced including H_2O, N_2, H_2, CO_2, and CO.

The quality of the gun cotton produced is dependent upon the temperature and time of contact of the reactants. The number of replacements by nitrate that occur depend upon these reaction variables.

Materials | Sulfuric acid, conc. 18 M, H_2SO_4 250-mL Beaker
Nitric acid, conc. 15 M, HNO_3 Pure cotton

Safety Precautions | The combustion is safe in small amounts but should be done on a non-combustible surface. Have a fire extinguisher handy.

The preparation is particularly dangerous since both concentrated sulfuric and nitric acids are being used and the reaction MUST be carried out below 40 °C. Nitric acid is corrosive; strong oxidant; toxic by inhalation; avoid contact with acetic acid and readily oxidized substances.

Sulfuric acid is severely corrosive to eyes, skin and other tissue. Wear chemical splash goggles, chemical-resistant gloves and a chemical-resistant apron.

Preparation | Preparation of gun cotton is easy, but time consuming. Slowly mix 75 mL of concentrated sulfuric acid with 25 mL concentrated nitric acid in a beaker and cool. React only pure cotton, absorbent cotton works best or pure cotton gauze will substitute.

Immerse the cotton, NO MORE THAN one gram at a time, in the acid solution for one to two minutes. Use of a cold water bath will help to keep the temperature down during nitration. Remove carefully, allowing the excess acid to drip off. Then drop into a large, one-liter beaker with running cold water for 5 to 10 minutes. Rinse the wet material with one molar bicarbonate solution. If no fizzing occurs, the acid is rinsed out. Air dry thoroughly.

Demonstration | To combust, place a small portion on a safe surface and touch with a hot stirring rod or a match.

Disposal | Neutralize all remaining acid and flush down the drain with acess water according to Flinn Suggested Disposal Method #24b.

Traffic Light Reaction

A yellow solution is swirled and turns red, then when shaken turns green.

Application	Redox • Organic Chemistry • Concentration
Theory	Indigo carmine solution is reduced by the alkaline dextrose solution causing it to turn yellow. As the flask is swirled oxygen dissolves into solution causing the indicator to be oxidized. As a result the indicator turns red. When the flask is vigorously shaken the increase in oxygen causes the indicator to further oxidize resulting in a green color being produced. Upon standing the oxygen concentration drops causing the indicator to return to its alkaline yellow. The yellow color may be attained sooner if the flask is shaken just until the red color appears, thereby limiting the amount of oxygen dissolved.
Materials	*Stop-'N-Go Light,* Flinn demo kit AP2083 or Dextrose (3 g) Sodium hydroxide, NaOH (5 g) 250-mL Flask Indigo carmine indicator, 1% solution (5–10 mL) Stopper
Safety Precautions	Indigo carmine indicator solution is toxic by ingestion. Sodium hydroxide is a corrosive solid; skin burns are possible; very dangerous to eyes. Always wear chemical splash goggles, chemical-resistant gloves and a chemical-resistant apron.
Preparation	Prepare a solution by dissolving 3 g of dextrose and 5 g sodium hydroxide in enough water to make 250 mL of solution. Pour this solution into a 250 mL flask. Add 5 to 10 mL indigo carmine indicator solution to this solution or until the solution is a consistent yellow color. It is important that only enough of the indicator is added to attain the yellow color. Stopper the flask.
Demonstration	Gently swirl the flask until a red color appears. Vigorously shake the flask until a green color appears. If the solution is allowed to stand, it will return to its original yellow color. For a variation of this reaction, air or oxygen gas may be bubbled through the solution in place of the swirling and shaking and a magnetic stirrer may be used.
Disposal	The solution may be flushed down the drain with excess water.
References	Summerlin, L., et al. *Chemical Demonstrations*; American Chemical Society: Washington, DC, 1988; Vol. 1, p 111. Abbott, C. E. *J. Chem. Ed.* **1948,** *26,* 100.

A Carbohydrate — How Sweet It Is!

Enzymes are used to extract sugars from soda crackers. The sugar is tested using Benedict's Solution.

Application

Biochemistry • Enzymes • Catalysts • Carbohydrates • Indicators • Sugars

Theory

Soda crackers taste sweet when eaten; however they contain no sugar. Saliva is used to convert the starch present in soda crackers into sugar. Starch is a polysaccharide which is a polymer of sugar—specifically glucose! Amylase, an enzyme found in saliva is responsible for catalyzing the reaction.

To monitor the reaction, Benedict's and Iodine solutions will be used. Iodine solution serves as an indicator of starch. Iodine forms a blue colored complex with starch. Benedict's solution is a glucose indicator. It turns yellow to red in color (depending on concentration) to indicate the presence of glucose.

Materials

Soda crackers
Zip-lock® bags
125-mL Flask with stopper
Test tubes (4)
Pipets
Distilled water
Iodine-starch indicator
Amylase solution
Benedict's solution
1000-mL Beaker
Hot plate

Safety Precautions

It is common practice not to consume food in a laboratory. In this experiment prepare individually wrapped crackers in Zip-lock bags in a sanitary environment. Students should remove the cracker and immediately consume it. Do not allow the food to come into contact with laboratory equipment. This demonstration is best done in a classroom away from chemicals. Wear chemical splash goggles and always follow laboratory safety rules while performing demonstrations.

Preparation

Prepare individual samples of crackers for tasting by placing one cracker in Zip-lock bag per person. Do not store these samples in a laboratory.

Demonstration

Review the ingredients of a box of saltines. Point out that sugar is not present as an ingredient. Emphasize that sugar is not an ingredient of soda crackers. Pass a few crackers around the room and have students verify that the crackers taste sweet.

Crush a cracker using a mortar and pestle and place in a 125-mL flask. Fill the flask with distilled water. Stopper the flask and shake well. Set aside.

Transfer 10 mL of the cracker solution to a test tube. Add 1 mL iodine solution to test for the presence of starch. The iodine solution should turn blue-black in color.

Label three test tubes 1, 2, and 3. Add the following:

Test Tube	2 mL Benedict's Solution	10 mL Cracker Solution	1 mL Amylase Solution
1 (control)	yes	yes	no
2 (control)	yes	no	yes
3	yes	yes	yes

Place the tubes in a hot water bath and heat for one minute. Upon heating the controls should observe no change. The tube containing the cracker and Amylase should develop a color change indicating the presence of glucose.

Note: This demonstration can also be performed using 5 mL saliva.

Disposal

The solution can be flushed down the drain with excess water.

Reference

Martin Stickle, Summit High School, Summit, NJ.

Chapter 7

Stoichiometry

Mole Samples

Visual samples of molar quantities help teach the concept.

Application | Mole • Molar Mass • Volume • Physical Properties

Theory | Due to density differences, molecular size differences, crystal latice packing, and water of hydration; molar quantities of compounds and elements vary widely when viewed from the perspective of space occupied. Though the number of particles in a mole of atoms or molecules is constant, they may have widely differing molar volumes.

Materials | Plastic bottles, with caps
Labels
Clear tape
Various elements and compounds

Safety Precautions | Wear chemical splash goggles and always follow laboratory safety rules while performing demonstrations.

Preparation | Label the bottles clearly with substance name, formula, formula mass, and mass of substance in the bottle. Weigh out one mole of six to ten substances of your choosing. It is recommended that you use some common substances such as water, some elements such as lead and aluminum, and some compounds such as glucose or sucrose and hydrated copper sulfate. Tape the caps onto the bottles.

Demonstration | Show one of the bottles pointing out what is on the label. Discuss the concept of the constant, Avogadro's number, N. Show another bottle noting the difference in the amount of substance present. Write the formulas on the board and point out the differences. Follow this with a rough sketch of the shape and size of the molecule. Use 3-D models if available. Call attention to number of atoms, sizes of atoms, arrangements of atoms, density differences and kinds of atoms present in each substance. Pass the bottles around the class so students can experience the differences.

Note: Possible student involvement could be setting up additional bottles by having them weigh samples. Hands-on activity might also have the students weigh out, in front of class, one mole of salt and one mole of sucrose.

Disposal | None required if the bottles are kept from year to year.

Conservation of Mass

The masses of two solutions are compared with their reaction products to illustrate the Law of Mass Conservation.

Application | Law of Mass Conservation • Chemical Reactions • Precipitation

Theory | During a chemical reaction, the quantity of matter is unchanged. That is, the mass of the reactants equals the mass of the products. The Law of Mass Conservation states that in any physical or chemical reaction, mass is neither created nor destroyed; it is conserved. In this reaction two solutions, lead (II) nitrate and sodium iodide, are mixed producing the yellow precipitate, lead (II) iodide in a solution of sodium nitrate:

$$Pb(NO_3)_2 + 2NaI \rightarrow PbI_2 + 2NaNO_3$$

Materials | Lead (II) nitrate, 0.1 M, $Pb(NO_3)_2$ (5 mL)
Sodium iodide, 0.2 M, NaI (5 mL)
250-mL Erlenmeyer flask
Small test tubes (both must fit into the flask) (2)
Stopper
Balance
Filtering apparatus

Safety Precautions | Lead nitrate is toxic by inhalation and ingestion, strong oxidant, and a dangerous fire risk when in contact with organic materials. Sodium iodide is moderately toxic. Wear chemical splash goggles, chemical-resistant gloves and a chemical-resistant apron.

Preparation | Prepare lead nitrate (3.3 g/100 mL H_2O) and sodium iodide (3 g/100 mL H_2O) Jsolutions.

Demonstration | Fill one test tube 3/4 full with lead (II) nitrate solution and the other with sodium iodide solution. While holding the test tubes upright, carefully slide them into the Erlenmeyer flask. Affix a rubber stopper to the flask.

Determine and record the mass of the flask and its contents. Invert the flask to allow the two solutions to mix. Mass the flask and its contents and compare this figure to the original measurement.

Disposal | Lead solutions and mixtures can be disposed of by Flinn Suggested Disposal Method #27f and all other solutions by flushing down the drain with excess water.

Have a Blast with Electrolysis

Identify the correct proportions of hydrogen and oxygen to create the largest explosion.

Application | Stoichiometry • Properties of Gases • Electrolysis • Density • Combustion

Theory | The electrolysis of water produces two volumes of pure hydrogen and one volume of pure oxygen:

$$2H_2O(l) \rightarrow 2H_2(g) + O_2(g)$$

The combustion of hydrogen is more explosive with pure oxygen than with air. The correct proportions of gases are obtained much more easily with Hoffman's electrolysis apparatus than from cylinders of gases or by other chemical reactions. Allowing the electrolysis apparatus to run for a minute or two before class will saturate the solution with the hydrogen and oxygen gas and show the 2:1 volumes more clearly.

Materials | Hoffman Electrolysis Apparatus
DC power source
Plastic bottle, 4–8 oz.
Duct or electrician's tape
Rubber stopper to fit bottle, 2-hole
Large beaker
Candle
Sulfuric acid, 0.1 M, H_2SO_4 (1 mL)

If a Hoffman's apparatus is not available, two burets inverted into a 600-mL beaker can be used.

Safety Precautions | Sulfuric acid is severely corrosive to eyes, skin and other tissue; considerable heat of dilution with water; even very dilute solutions are harmful to eyes and skin.

Never use a glass bottle! Do not use a bottle larger than 8 oz. Inspect the plastic bottle for any cracks prior to demonstration. Never re-use a plastic bottle as this type of explosion will produce small cracks throughout the bottle that are not visible to the unaided eye. Warn the students to cover their ears. Be sure that the power source is properly grounded. Wear chemical splash goggles, chemical-resistant gloves and a chemical-resistant apron.

Preparation | Prepare collection bottle by wrapping it tightly with a layer of duct or electrician's tape. This tape will add strength to the bottle. To a Hoffman's electrolysis apparatus add a few mL of 0.1 M H_2SO_4 diluted with distilled water. Any DC power source can then be used to do the electrolysis of the water.

Demonstration	Connect the power source and generate the oxygen and hydrogen gases.
	Fill a 4-oz. plastic bottle with water and affix a 2-hole rubber stopper. Disconnect the power source from the apparatus to prevent any chance of shock. Invert the bottle and insert one of the two stopcocks of the apparatus into one of the holes. Holding the bottle in place, use the stopcocks to fill the bottle with the hydrogen and oxygen generated by the Hoffman's electrolysis apparatus (using a water displacement method). Allow the displaced water to leak down the apparatus into a large beaker or dish placed under the apparatus. If necessary, repeat these steps until the bottle is completely filled. Once the bottle is filled, place your fingers over the holes of the stopper to prevent the gases from leaking out. (Hydrogen is less dense than air, whereas oxygen has a density greater than air.)
	To demonstrate the combustion of the gas mixture, unstopper the bottle and immediately hold the mouth of the bottle to the flame of a candle. Hold the bottle with beaker tongs.
Disposal	The solution can be flushed down the drain with excess water.
Reference	Alyea, H. *Tested Demonstrations in Chemistry,* 6th ed.; Journal of Chemical Education; Easton, PA, 1965.

Hydrogen Bomb

A demonstration of the stoichiometric combustion of hydrogen gas.

Application   Stoichiometry • Explosions • Gases • Reactivity • Combustion

Theory   A two-liter soda bottle, with the bottom cut out, is fitted with a one-hole rubber stopper which holds the glass tip of a dropper. The bottle is filled with hydrogen gas by the downward displacement of air. The hydrogen gas is ignited and slowly burns in the presence of oxygen from the air outside of the bottle. The burning of the gas causes a whistling sound to be emitted through the glass orifice. As the hydrogen gas is consumed the bottle slowly fills with air through the bottom opening. As the hydrogen concentration decreases the whistle diminishes and the flame grows weak. Eventually the flame is drawn into the bottle which causes the hydrogen–air mixture within to explode with a bright yellow light.

When ignited the hydrogen reacts with oxygen to produce water vapor:

$$2H_2 + O_2 \rightarrow 2H_2O$$

Materials   Two-liter plastic soda bottle, with bottom removed
Stopper to fit bottle, 1-hole
Glass tube from medicine dropper
Hydrogen gas
Ring stand and clamp

Safety Precautions   Hydrogen gas is very flammable and yields explosive mixtures with air. Do not have any open flames while filling plastic bottle. If using a gas cylinder, secure tank to wall to prevent accidental tipping. Students should be warned of explosive noise and told to cup hands over ears. Do not use a glass bottle for this demonstration. Wear chemical splash goggles, chemical-resistant gloves and a chemical-resistant apron.

Preparation   Cut off the bottom of a two-liter soda bottle. Insert the glass tube of a medicine dropper in the hole of a 1-hole stopper, with the thin stem pointed out. Secure the stopper on the soda bottle. Clamp the bottle to a ring stand.

Demonstration   Fill the bottle with hydrogen gas through the bottom. Set the hydrogen cylinder aside. Ignite the hydrogen at the tip of the glass tube. A blue flame should be visible. The whistle should diminish prior to explosion.

Disposal   None required.

Reference   This demonstration was presented by Ron Perkins during the Fundamentals Institute at the Institute for Chemical Education; University of Wisconsin—Madison, July, 1989.

Catalytic Copper

Demonstrate a reaction between two solids.

Application	Chemical Reactions • Stoichiometry • Catalysis • Redox
Theory	The reaction of copper and sulfur is stoichiometric:

$$Cu + S \xrightarrow{CuSO_4} CuS$$

Copper sulfate acts as a catalyst, but the mechanism is not understood. The catalytic effect may be verified by trying the reaction in boiling water instead, there will be no reaction. The reaction is a good example of a reaction between two solids.

Materials

Cupric sulfate, 0.1 M, $CuSO_4$
Powdered copper
Powdered sulfur
500-mL Erlenmeyer flask
Hot plate or Bunsen burner
Magnetic stirrer or stirring rod

Safety Precautions

Finely divided sulfur can be a moderate fire or explosion risk. Sulfur has low toxicity but may be a skin irritant. Copper, in a finely divided form, presents a serious fire and explosion risk. Cupric sulfate is a skin and respiratory irritant, toxic by ingestion and inhalation. Wear chemical splash goggles, chemical-resistant gloves and a chemical-resistant apron.

Preparation

Prepare cupric sulfate solution. This is not a critical concentration, dissolve about 1 tsp. of the hydrated crystals in 200 mL water.

Demonstration

Bring 200 mL of the cupric sulfate solution to a boil in the 500-mL flask. Mix 6.4 g of powdered copper and 3.2 g of powdered sulfur. Stir this mixture into the cupric sulfate solution. Continue stirring as the mixture boils. A black solid (CuS) forms and settles to the bottom of the flask.

Disposal

Filter CuS mixture, then dispose of solid residue in the trash and the copper sulfate solution by washing down the drain with excess water.

Reference

Summerlin, L., et al. *Chemical Demonstrations;* American Chemical Society: Washington, DC, 1988; Vol. 2, p 149.

Alternative Fuels — The Methanol Car

Useful as a combustion demo and to demonstrate the physical forces produced through combustion and gas expansion.

Application	Gas Properties • Combustion • Energy
Theory	This demo uses the combustion of methanol. Expanding gases, directed backward, will result in the car being propelled forward. Good demo for an action–reaction discussion.
Materials	5-gal Water cooler plastic bottle (never use glass!)* Large dynamics cart, 30 cm long Duct tape or latex tubing, 60 cm Wooden board, 30 × 30 cm Large ring stand with utility clamp Wooden splint or candle Meter stick or dowel, 1 m long *Replace bottle after about four uses due to chemical changes in the plastic caused by heat.
Safety Precautions	Do not ignite the methanol–air mixture with a match, always use an ignition stick. Always use a deflector, such as a wooden board, which is securely clamped to a fixed object. Repeated use of the bottle may cause some chemical changes in the plastic. Bottles have been known to shatter. Wear chemical splash goggles, chemi-cal-resistant gloves and a chemical-resistant apron.
Preparation	To construct the methanol car, strap a water cooler bottle to a dynamics cart (from the physics lab). The bottle may be strapped to the cart using duct tape or heavy latex tubing. Be certain the bottle is strapped securely at least at two separate points. The deflector plate may be made from a piece of lumber with minimum dimensions of 30 × 30 cm which is firmly affixed to a stationary object. It is important to use a deflector, as the flames produced will burn the paint off a wall. The igniter stick may be made by affixing a wooden splint or candle to the end of a meter stick. Never light the bottle with a match.
Demonstration	Pour about 5 to 10 mL methanol into the vehicle. (Using ethanol will result in a greater amount of force due the greater volume of gases produced). Swirl the methanol until the walls of the bottle are coated. Pour out any excess liquid and wipe the mouth of the bottle dry. Set the vehicle with the end a few centimeters away from the deflector board. Have students stand behind the intended path of the vehicle. Using an ignition stick, carefully ignite the vapor escaping the bottle. The alcohol–air mixture should ignite and propel the bottle away from the deflector plate. The procedure may be repeated only if a fresh sample of air is introduced. This may be done using a bicycle pump. Do not use an oxygen tank because the mixture may cause the bottle to explode.
Disposal	None required.

Fingerprint Detective

Fingerprints contain amino acids and respond to the ninhydrin test.

Application	Organic Chemistry • Amino Acids • Indicators
Theory	Ninhydrin reacts with amino acids found in the natural oils left by fingers to produce a pinkish-purple color. The intensity of the color is also a quantitative indicator of the amount of amino acids present.
Materials	Paper Ninhydrin, 0.5% solution, (Flinn N0039) Spray bottle (e.g., fine mist hair spray bottle) Hot plate or high temperature hair dryer
Safety Precautions	Ninhydrin is an irritant, biologically active, and is dissolved in flammable butanol. Butanol is also an irritant. Work in a hood or well ventilated area. Hold paper with forceps while spraying. Wear chemical splash goggles, chemical-resistant gloves and a chemical-resistant apron.
Preparation	If available, have some pure amino acids to show effect. Put some nice, heavy fingerprints on the paper. Have ninhydrin in spray bottle. Heat up hot plate if used. Not necessary for hair dryer.
Demonstration	Work in a hood or well ventilated area. Spray the paper containing amino acids and/or heavy fingerprints lightly, but thoroughly with the ninhydrin spray. Dry. When dry, hold the paper above the heat source (about 10 cm.) Do not scorch. Pinkish color will appear. Have a student place fingerprints on another piece of paper. Repeat above.
Disposal	Papers may be disposed of in the trash. Ninhydrin will store well.
Reference	*A Sourcebook for the Biological Sciences,* 2nd Ed.; Harcourt Brace Jovanovich: New York, 1966; p 138.

Chapter 8

Phases of Matter

Riding on Air

Soap bubbles at the juncture of chilled carbon dioxide layer will gradually expand.

Application	Gases • Solubility • Equilibrium • Density • Refraction of Light
Theory	Carbon dioxide is highly soluble in water. As the soap bubbles are introduced into the container of carbon dioxide gas, the carbon dioxide quickly begins to dissolve into the soap solution of the bubble. Since the bubble is surrounded by a high concentration of carbon dioxide and the interior of the bubble has a low concentration of carbon dioxide, some of the gas moves into the bubble itself in order to reach an equilibrium of concentration. As the amount of gas within the bubble increases, pressure causes the bubble to expand. As it expands, an ever-changing colored pattern begins to develop on the surface of the bubble. These patterns are a result of light being refracted due to the changing curvature of the bubble. Throughout the demonstration the soap bubbles will float at the juncture of the chilled carbon dioxide as the carbon dioxide is denser than the overall density of the soap bubbles.
Materials	Soap solution Glycerin (5 mL) Soap bubble wand Aquarium Dry ice pellets (2 kg), see pg. xiv.
Safety Precautions	Handle dry ice with gloves. Never place dry ice in a sealed container! Wear chemical splash goggles and always follow laboratory safety rules while performing demonstrations.
Preparation	Add 2 mL glycerin to every 200 mL commercial soap solution. The glycerin prolongs the life of the bubble. Place about 2 kg dry ice into the bottom of an aquarium and allow it to stand for ten minutes.
Demonstration	Pour some of the carbon dioxide gas out of the aquarium so that only the bottom half contains carbon dioxide. Blow one or two soap bubbles into the aquarium. Observe. You should expect that the bubbles will float at the carbon dioxide–air interface. Within a minute, the bubbles will develop a purplish sheen that will gradually change in shade. If the bubbles remain long enough the soap–water mixture may actually freeze leaving a solid bubble.
Disposal	Allow excess dry ice to sublime.
Reference	Alyea, H. N. *Tested Demonstrations in Chemistry;* Journal of Chemical Education: Easton, PA, 1965; p 36.

Boiling Cold, Freezing Hot

Hot and cold are relative terms and even ice can boil a liquid.

Application	Liquid Nitrogen • Physical Properties • Freezing Point • Boiling Point
Theory	The terms, hot and cold are relative terms. Water may be cold, but ice is colder. It may be a hot day, but boiling water is hotter. Liquid nitrogen has a boiling point of −196 °C. When liquid nitrogen comes into contact with any object at a higher temperature it will boil vigorously. This is analogous to having water coming into contact with an object at a higher temperature than its boiling point—it will also vigorously boil. A substance need not be "hot" to boil—it only has to be hot enough.
Materials	Whistling tea kettles (2) Distilled water Ice, large block Hot plate Liquid nitrogen, see pg. xiv. Shallow dishpan or cookie sheet
Safety Precautions	Use extreme care while handling liquid nitrogen. This extremely cold substance can cause frostbite when it, or anything that has been immersed in it, comes in contact with your skin. Wearing a pair of protective gloves to protect your skin is a wise idea. Never store liquid nitrogen in a container with a tight fitting lid. Wear chemical splash goggles and follow laboratory safety rules while performing demonstrations.
Demonstration	Place a whistling tea kettle containing water on a hot plate (have the water preheated to just under the boiling point prior to presentation). Place another whistling tea kettle containing liquid nitrogen on a large block of ice. Observe that both kettles contain a boiling liquid. Notes: It is advisable to keep the liquid nitrogen-filled kettle in a Styrofoam® cooler filled 2 to 3 cm deep with liquid nitrogen, until ready for the presentation. This will keep the kettle from whistling prior to being placed on the block of ice.
Disposal	Liquid nitrogen can be left to boil away.
Reference	Institute for Chemical Education, University of Wisconsin, Summer 1989.

Cryogenic Malleability

Liquid nitrogen is used to lower the temperature of various substances revealing changes in their malleability.

Application | Liquid Nitrogen • Cryogenics • Malleability • Ductility • Metals

Theory | Liquid nitrogen is prepared by first condensing air. Since air is a mixture of 78% N_2 and 21% O_2 and 1% other gases, the nitrogen must be separated by fractional distillation. Oxygen has a boiling point of –183 °C; and nitrogen, at –196 °C will boil off first. Liquid nitrogen is used extensively as a freezing agent in the food-processing and medical industries and as a medium to lower the temperature of materials and devices used in certain scientific research when low temperatures are desired. Unlike other substances, nitrogen is unreactive which explains its widespread usage.

When objects are introduced into cryogenic liquids, their malleability and ductility are dramatically changed. The overall flexibility of a flower or banana is lost because the water within the object freezes producing a rigid ice-crystal network. The flower breaks easily since the crystals are thin whereas the banana remains intact since the network is large. The rubber ball and lead spring are each made of a single substance which exhibit different elastic properties at different temperatures.

The term malleability refers to the property that allows an object to be bent, flattened or shaped. The composition of a malleable object is such that its atoms or molecules are loosely held allowing freer movement about each other. Ductility refers to the property that allows an object to be stretched. As in malleable objects, the atoms or molecules of a ductile piece of matter are loosely held allowing the object to be stretched. As the temperature of a malleable or ductile object decreases its degree of malleability also decreases because of the decrease in kinetic energy of the atoms within the object.

Materials | Liquid nitrogen, 5 L, see p. xvi.
Work gloves
Dewar flask
Styrofoam® coffee cups
Tongs
Flower
Hollow rubber ball (e.g., racquetball)
Banana
Block of pine (approx. $10 \times 10 \times 2$ cm)
Common nail, 10 penny
Lead wire, 50 cm (2)
Ring stand, with ring
Paper clips (2)
500-g Hooked balance masses (2)

Safety Precautions

Use extreme care while handling liquid nitrogen. This extremely cold substance can cause frostbite when it, or anything that has been immersed in it, comes in contact with your skin. Wearing a pair of protective gloves to protect your skin is a wise idea. Never store liquid nitrogen in a container with a tight fitting lid. Wear chemical splash goggles and follow laboratory safety rules while performing demonstrations.

Preparation

Coil two 50-cm pieces of lead wire around a pencil making it appear like a spring. Loop each end of the coils such that they may be hung from a hook.

Demonstration

Freezing a Flower: Fill a Styrofoam coffee cup half full of liquid nitrogen. Immerse a small flower in the liquid nitrogen for about ten seconds. Remove flower and proceed to break off the petals using a pair of tongs.

Nailing With Bananas: Fill a Styrofoam coffee cup half full of liquid nitrogen. Immerse one end of a banana in the liquid nitrogen for about three minutes. Remove the banana, and using its frozen end, proceed to hammer a nail into a wooden board.

Rubber Losing Its Elasticity: Fill a Styrofoam cup half full of liquid nitrogen. Immerse a hollow rubber ball in the liquid nitrogen for about three minutes. Remove the frozen ball and compare its appearance to a rubber ball at room temperature. Drop both balls on a hard surface at the same time.

A Lead Spring: Hang one of the lead coils from a paper clip hook from the ring stand. Fill a Styrofoam coffee cup half full of liquid nitrogen. Immerse the other coil in the liquid nitrogen for about three minutes. Remove the coil and hang it from the second paper clip hook on the ring stand. Attach a 500-g mass to each of the coils. Observe that the cooled lead coil has developed the property of elasticity.

Disposal

Liquid nitrogen can be left to boil away. Dispose of the broken flower petals and banana in the trash as soon as possible. Cleanup is a problem once the petals and banana have thawed.

How Ice Skates Work

Demonstrate the effect of pressure on the freezing point of a substance.

Application	Freezing Point • Pressure
Theory	When enough pressure is applied to a solid its freezing point will drop. This principle explains how ice skates work. As a skater glides along an ice rink, the small surface area of the skate blade applies a great pressure to the surface of the ice. At the point where the blade touches the ice, the ice will melt. In fact, the skater is not skating on ice but gliding on a thin layer of liquid water. As the blade moves along the path of melted ice, the liquid water re-freezes instantly. This is known as regelation. People who live in cold climates, such as in northern Canada find it difficult to skate on extremely cold days, as the pressure of the skate blades is not large enough to affect the extra cold ice.
Materials	Cylinder of ice, 30 × 3 cm o.d. Ring stands (2) Insulated clamps (2) 1-kg masses (2) Thin, strong wire, e.g., piano or guitar wire (50 cm)
Safety Precautions	Wear chemical splash goggles and always follow laboratory safety rules while performing demonstrations.
Preparation	Prepare a cylinder of ice, or freeze a water balloon inside a paper towel tube. Clamp a 30 cm long by 3 cm diameter cylinder of ice from both ends. Two clamps and ring stands should be used. It is advisable to use rubber insulated clamps to prevent the clamps from melting the ice. Attach two 1-kg masses to each end of a strong, thin 50 cm wire. Keep the ice cylinder in a cooler with ice until ready for the demonstration.
Demonstration	Suspend this weighted wire over the cylinder. The weight of the masses will pull the wire right through the ice in about five minutes and will fall with a crash. As the wire moves through the ice the ice will re-freeze in its path.
Disposal	None required.
Reference	Barron, P. *The Science Teacher,* **1982,** *49,* 54.

Preparation of Liquid Oxygen

Demonstrate the effect of a high concentration of oxygen on the rate of combustion.

Application | Liquid Nitrogen • Combustion

Theory | Liquid oxygen has a boiling point of –183 °C. The liquid may be attained using liquid nitrogen (boiling point –196 °C) to condense oxygen from a tank. The characteristic blue color of oxygen will also be displayed.

Materials

Liquid nitrogen, see pg. xiv.	500-mL Styrofoam® cup
Pyrex® test tube	Glass tubing (10 cm)
Rubber stopper, 2-hole	Candle
Oxygen tank	Fire extinguisher
Latex tubing	Matches
Tongs	250-mL Beaker

Safety Precautions

Use extreme care while handling liquid nitrogen. This extremely cold substance can cause frostbite when it, or anything that has been immersed in it, comes in contact with your skin. Wearing a pair of protective gloves to protect your skin is a wise idea. Never store liquid nitrogen in a container with a tight fitting lid. Wear chemical splash goggles and follow laboratory safety rules while performing demonstrations.

Liquid oxygen has the capability to support violent combustion—even with substances that normally do not burn. Keep open flames away from the liquid oxygen. Choose an appropriate place to allow the oxygen to evaporate when disposing. Never leave liquid oxygen unattended. Always have a fire extinguisher handy.

Preparation

Fill a 500-mL Styrofoam cup half full of liquid nitrogen. Affix a 2-hole stopper to a large glass Pyrex test tube. The stopper should have a short glass tube extending out of one of the holes. Attach a hose to the glass tube and run it to an oxygen tank.

Demonstration

Allow the oxygen to slowly bleed into the test tube. Be certain that the second hole in the stopper remains open, to allow the excess gas to escape. The oxygen should condense along the walls of the test tube. Note the blue color of the liquid.

Pour the liquid oxygen into a pre-cooled 250-mL beaker. The beaker may be cooled by rinsing with liquid nitrogen. Toss a small lighted candle or match into the beaker —it should be consumed immediately.

Disposal | Allow the oxygen and nitrogen to evaporate.

Anti-Bubbles

Generate spherical envelopes of gas that are bounded on both sides by a liquid.

Application	Density • Gas Properties
Theory	Normal bubbles are spherical envelopes of liquid (often soapy water) that are bounded inside and out by a gas. Anti-bubbles are spherical envelopes of gas that are bounded on both sides by a liquid.
Materials	1000-mL Beaker 50-mL Beaker Clear dishwashing detergent
Safety Precautions	Wear chemical splash goggles and always follow laboratory safety rules while performing demonstrations.
Preparation	Practice!!
Demonstration	Fill (to near overflowing) a 1000-mL beaker with cold tap water. If there are air bubbles in the water, let the beaker stand until they dissipate. Pour about 1 mL of the detergent into the water. Gently stir the mixture. Try not to make any normal bubbles on the surface.
	Measure out 30 to 40 mL of the soapy liquid into the 50-mL beaker. Pour small portions of the soapy liquid into the large beaker. The height from which this is done is critical. The base of the 50-mL beaker should almost touch the surface of the liquid in the large beaker. You may have to practice the pouring. The liquid should not be delivered in a steady stream, but rather in small portions with a jerky motion. (One student described it as "glopping".)
	Anti-bubbles can be easily recognized. They move slowly downward when formed then slowly climb toward the surface. They will stay fully below the surface. The average life span of an anti-bubble is 1 to 2 min. If a drop of food coloring is added to the liquid in the 50-mL beaker, the anti-bubbles will have colored centers, thus proving to the unbelievers that they are, in fact not just air bubbles. A more startling effect can be achieved by dissolving some NaCl in the liquid in the 50-mL beaker. This will increase the density of the solution, and if enough salt is added, the density of the anti-bubbles will exceed the density of the soapy water and the anti-bubbles will sink to the bottom of the large beaker.
Disposal	All solutions can be safely flushed down the drain.
Reference	Becker, B. *Twenty Demonstrations Guaranteed to Knock Your Socks Off!*; Flinn Scientific: Batavia, IL, 1994.

Chapter 9

Gas Laws

Cartesian Diver

Construct and demonstrate a Cartesian diver.

Application

Density • Pressure • Boyle's Law

Theory

Since liquids are not compressible, any pressure exerted on a liquid is instantly transmitted throughout the liquid. Gas volumes vary inversely with pressure (Boyle's Law). Increasing pressure on the container will compress the air trapped in the Cartesian diver, causing some water to enter. This increases the density of the diver, causing it to sink. Releasing the pressure on the container reverses the procedure, and the diver rises.

Materials

2-L Soda bottle with cap
Beral-type Pipet, thin stem
Hex nuts, 6×32
Acetate transparency sheets (optional)
Scissors
Copper or stainless steel wire
Hot-melt glue gun

Safety Precautions

Wear chemical splash goggles and always follow laboratory safety rules while performing demonstrations.

Preparation

Cut the stem of the Pipet to about 1 cm long. Wedge the hex nut onto the stem. This becomes the diver. A dab of hot glue might be needed to keep it in place, if so, be careful not to block the Pipet opening with glue. Form a loop of fine wire and glue it to the top of the Pipet bulb. Use a beaker filled with water to adjust the density of the Pipet by partially filling it with water. The diver should just barely float. Fill the 2-L bottle with water, place the diver inside and cap. A gentle squeeze on the bottle should cause the diver to sink, and when the squeezing is stopped, the diver will rise. Construct a second diver in the same manner and adjust the buoyancy so that it just sinks. Construct a third diver with a small hook made of the fine wire on the stem end of the Pipet. Adjust the buoyancy so this diver just floats. Put both divers into another 2-L bottle full of water and now try to manipulate so that the diver with the hook can retrieve the sunken diver by engaging the loop.

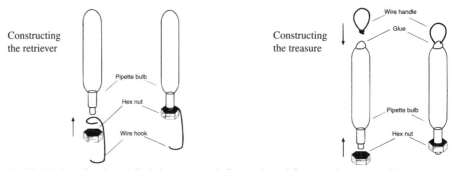

Constructing the retriever

Constructing the treasure

Wire handle

Glue

Pipette bulb

Hex nut

Wire hook

Demonstration	Demonstrate the single diver to the students. Pass it around so that they can try it. Point out that they should be able to see the water level changing in the Pipet as the bottle is squeezed and when the pressure is released. Have a competition to see if any students can successfully retrieve the sunken diver in the second bottle. Encourage students to construct their own diver. Another variation is to cut a small propeller out of the acetate sheet and place it on the stem of the Pipet before securing the nut in place. This will cause the diver to rotate as it sinks. A competition could involve making a diver that makes the greatest number of revolutions as it travels down to the bottom of the bottle and back up to the top. Encourage student experimentation. (Remember those magic words "extra credit".)
Disposal	None required.
Reference	Becker, R. *Twenty Demonstrations Guaranteed to Knock Your Socks Off!;* Flinn Scientific: Batavia, IL, 1994; p 40.

Knock Your Socks Off

The acetylene cannon is an exciting starting point for organic chemistry.

Application Combustion • Organic Chemistry • Oxidation

Theory This is a basic combustion of a hydrocarbon demo. It may be used as an inexpensive replacement for the Big Bang Cannon demo. Acetylene (ethyne) is produced by the reaction of water with calcium carbide in a semi-closed container. When the reaction proceeds long enough (10 to 15 seconds), the air–acetylene mixture is ignited.

$$CaC_2 + 2H_2O \rightarrow C_2H_2 + Ca(OH)_2$$
$$2C_2H_2 + 5O_2 \rightarrow 4CO_2 + 2H_2O + energy$$

Materials Acetylene cannon
Sock
Calcium carbide
Thin-stem Pipet
Distilled water

Note: You must build the apparatus. It is inexpensive and easy.

You need:
PVC pipe — 18–24″ long
PVC adapter/clean-out
PVC clean-out plug
PVC cement
Electric drill

All of these items are available at local hardware stores for about $10. Be certain that the plug has a hollow section on the inside, and that it threads easily into the adapter.

Safety Precautions This is a violent explosion. Warn observers of this and demonstrate the proper way to cover ears. Keep the "gun" nearly vertical. DO NOT overload with calcium carbide. Do not attempt to launch any object heavier or harder than a sock! Exposure of calcium carbide to water evolves flammable acetylene gas. Wear chemical splash goggles and always follow laboratory safety rules while performing demonstrations.

Preparation Build acetylene cannon (see figure) and practice.

Acetylene Cannon

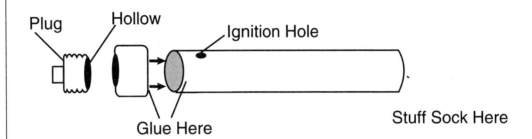

Demonstration

After you have glued the "gun" together, unscrew the plug, place one gram (maximum) of carbide into the hollow and screw back onto the adapter end of the pipe.

Add one thin-stem Pipet full (about 1–3 mL) of water through the touch-hole directly into the hollow well of the cap. The reaction will begin immediately. Stuff an old, rolled-up sock into the open end of the pipe. Lean the plugged end in the sink or other safe spot and use an ignition stick to ignite at the touch-hole. Work quickly—about 20 s following the addition of water.

Disposal

Flush residue down a drain after all signs of reaction have ceased.

Reference

This idea was first presented to us by Ed Brogie of Laurel-Concord School, Laurel, NE.

Break the Ruler

The force of air pressure is used to break a wooden ruler.

Application | Air Pressure • Inertia • Gases

Theory | Matter takes up space and has mass and inertia. The law of inertia states that matter in motion tends to stay in motion; matter at rest tends to remain at rest. The force of the blow acts for such a short period of time, that the air's inertia is not overcome. This results in the newspaper staying in place—holding the end of the ruler. Air pressure is approximately 15 pounds per square inch, so a sheet of newspaper would actually experience about 5000 pounds of force!

Materials | Inexpensive wooden ruler
Newspaper

Safety Precautions | Keep students well back as the ruler will break and the pieces may be flung a distance. Wear chemical splash goggles and always follow laboratory safety rules while performing demonstrations.

Demonstration | Lay a thin wooden ruler on the edge of a table such that about one-third of it extends off the edge. Cover the other end with a sheet of paper. With a closed fist strike the extended end of the ruler with a downward blow. The ruler should break leaving the newspaper unchanged.

Disposal | Pieces of the ruler can be discarded in the trash.

Crush the Can

Air pressure is used to crush an aluminum can.

Application	Pressure • Properties of Gases • Gas Laws
Theory	Air is matter, as it has mass and takes up space. Since it has mass it exerts pressure. If a partial vacuum is formed in a soda can, air pressure will crush the can. The vacuum is produced by the rapid condensation of steam within the can. The volume reduction from the gaseous state is a factor of between 600 to 1000.
Materials	Aluminum soda cans Hot plate Shallow pan or dish Beaker tongs
Safety Precautions	Wear chemical splash goggles and always follow laboratory safety rules while performing demonstrations.
Demonstration	Fill a shallow dish with water. Pour about 10 mL of water into a soda can and heat until the water boils. Quickly invert the soda can into the pan of water such that the opening is immersed under the water. The can will instantly collapse under the pressure of air.
Disposal	Used cans should be recycled.

Carbon Dioxide Cannon

Combining two household chemicals leads to a simple and relatively safe "explosion".

Application	Stoichiometry • Organic Chemistry • Gas Law • Consumer Chemistry
Theory	The reaction of acetic acid and sodium bicarbonate releases carbon dioxide which rapidly pushes a stopper from a plastic bottle.

$$NaHCO_3 + CH_3COOH \rightarrow CO_2 + H_2O + Na^+ + CH_3COO^-$$

The large volume of gas released by the reaction causes a sudden increase in pressure due to the limited space of the container. This relationship is referred to as Boyle's Law, $PV = k$. The Ideal Gas Law, $PV = nRT$ may also be tested using stoichiometric quantities.

If 25 g of baking soda is reacted with 50 mL vinegar (1 M) you may also discuss and demonstrate limiting reagents.

Materials	Plastic soda bottle, 500-mL Cork to fit, not a rubber stopper Baking soda, $NaHCO_3$ Vinegar, CH_3COOH
Safety Precautions	Never aim the cork at anyone! Do not use a glass bottle. Do not push cork too hard into bottle. Do not reuse the bottle more than a few times. Wear chemical splash goggles and always follow laboratory safety rules while performing demonstrations.
Preparation	Place 25 g baking soda in a tissue or other absorbent paper before placing into plastic bottle. The tissue slows the reaction rate down to allow more time to place the cork without significant loss of carbon dioxide gas. Place baking soda in bottom of bottle.
Demonstration	Pour 50 mL vinegar into the plastic bottle containing the baking soda and quickly push the cork into the bottle. Give the bottle a quick shake and set it on a table. Stand back and wait for the explosion.
Disposal	Solution can be disposed of by flushing down the drain with excess water.

Plenty Powerful Ping-Pong Popper

The combustion of methanol is used to propel a Ping-Pong® ball.

Application | Combustion • Gas Laws • Activation Energy

Theory | This is a basic combustion of methanol (ethanol) explosion demo. The expanding gases are used to propel a Ping-Pong ball.

Materials | Methanol or ethanol
Battery filler bulb
Lantern lighter
Ping-Pong ball

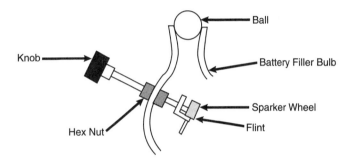

Safety Precautions | Ethanol and methanol are extremely flammable and dangerous fire risks, and toxic by ingestion. Beware of fumes from residual fuel in the bulb or from spilled alcohol. Never aim this at anyone! Wear chemical splash goggles and always follow laboratory safety rules while performing demonstrations.

Preparation | The device is made by purchasing a battery filler bulb at an auto accessory store and a lantern lighter from a camping store. Cost is about $2 for the bulb and about $5 for the lighter.

Buy cheap Ping-Pong balls. Never leave the ball in the bulb. It will dissolve.

Demonstration | Add about 1 mL of alcohol to the bulb. Do not get the flint wet. Place the Ping-Pong ball firmly into the mouth of the bulb. A quick twist of the knob will produce a spark for ignition. Snuff the remaining flame in the rubber bulb by placing the hand over the opening to cut off air supply.

Alternate demonstration: Simply squeeze the bulb firmly to pop the ball into the air. A sure shot Boyle's Law demo.

Disposal | Save the devise for future demos after allowing alcohol to evaporate in a fume hood.

Reference | Ron Crampton, Westside High School, Omaha, NE.

Charles' Law

Gases are liquified by cooling and compressing, a good demo of Charles' Law.

Application | Gases • Gas Properties • Gas Laws • Liquid Nitrogen

Theory | Liquid nitrogen has a boiling point of −196 °C and can be used to freeze many substances. Gases can be liquefied by cooling and compressing. Charles' Law states that volume and temperature of gases are directly proportional. As the air in a balloon is cooled, its volume decreases, according to Charles' Law which is $V = kT$.

Materials | 10-inch balloon (10)
Styrofoam® cooler
Dewar flask
Liquid nitrogen, see p. xiv.

Safety Precautions | Use extreme care while handling liquid nitrogen. This extremely cold substance can cause frostbite when it, or anything that has been immersed in it, comes in contact with your skin. Wearing a pair of protective gloves to protect your skin is a wise idea. Never store liquid nitrogen in a container with a tight fitting lid. Wear chemical splash goggles and follow laboratory safety rules while performing demonstrations.

Preparation | Pour about 500 mL of liquid nitrogen into a Styrofoam cooler. Lightly cover and allow to sit for about ten minutes. To add some intrigue, keep the contents of the cooler a mystery.

Demonstration | Have some students blow up and tie about ten balloons. Position the cooler on a stool above a table such that the contents of the cooler will not be visible to students. Have students approach the cooler one at a time and drop their balloon into the cooler. Students will quickly notice that the total volume of balloons far exceeds the volume of the cooler—yet all of the balloons fit into the cooler. Have students present their theories that explain the phenomenon.

Disposal | Allow excess liquid nitrogen to evaporate slowly in its container.

Chapter 10

Atomic Structure and Bonding

Rutherford Scattering

Demonstrate Rutherford Scattering using Ping-Pong balls and a model of an atom.

Application   Atomic Theory • Atomic Structure • Atoms

Theory   When Rutherford "shot" alpha particles at a thin sheet of gold foil, he observed that most of the "bullets" passed straight through without interference, disproving the notion that the atom was a solid sphere. A few of the particles, however, veered off to the sides and even fewer bounced straight back.

The conclusion was that the atom was mostly empty space with a tiny, positively charged, dense central particle called the nucleus. The alpha particles that veered off were deflected by the charge as they came too close to the nucleus while those that came back, actually "bounced" off of the nucleus.

Materials   Black box–gold foil sample
Ping-Pong® balls (about 10)
Plywood, 45 × 45 cm
Wood dowels, (4)
   or
Cardboard box, 18 × 18 in. square

Safety Precautions   No special precautions are needed for this demo, but always follow laboratory safety rules while performing demonstrations.

Preparation   Prepare a "black box" to simulate the gold foil as follows: Take a rectangular piece of plywood or cardboard about 45 cm on a side (a soda flat works well and is readily available). Fasten to the center of the cardboard a target of about 0.5 cm diameter that will be hot glued or fastened firmly so that its location is not obvious to the student observers. Raise the board high enough off the floor so a Ping-Pong ball will readily roll in one side and out the other. Corner supports may be made from pieces of dowel or small blocks of wood. If a soda flat is used, the corners may be cut about 1 cm on a side before removing the side panels. See the diagram below.

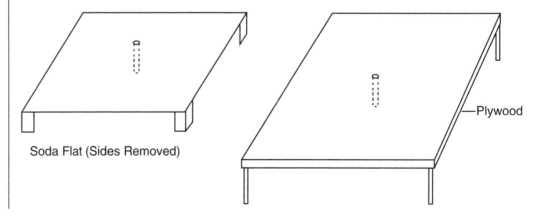

Soda Flat (Sides Removed)

Plywood

An alternative, more permanent board may be made of plywood with the target inserted into a shallow hole drilled halfway through the board. It may be supported on the corners with other pieces of dowel.

Procedure

Place the board on the floor. Have the students stand around the periphery where it is clearly visible to them.

Roll the Ping-Pong balls rapidly under one side of the board permitting them to come out the other side or ends. It is best to roll toward a wall to stop the balls.

Observe what happens to the balls that hit the target directly and those that are deflected off the sides of the target.

Alternative activities might include plotting the paths to show the low frequency of hits. Try to have students predict where the target is and how big it is. Remember, don't show them what is really there, this is a black box.

Disposal

None. Save the apparatus for next class and next year.

Reference

George Gross, Union High School, Union, New Jersey.

Heisenberg's Uncertainty Principle

Demonstrate some of the reasoning behind the uncertainty principle.

Application Atomic Structure • Atomic Theory • Electrons

Theory Heisenberg's Uncertainty Principle is very important to our understanding of the concept of the electron cloud, and the reason why we do not consider electrons to be in definite orbits. The Principle states that accurate determinations of the position and momentum of an electron cannot be made simultaneously. This can be a difficult concept for students to grasp. This demonstration shows that attempting to do this produces large uncertainties in one or the other quantity. For ease of demonstration, we use velocity (v), instead of momentum, (m • v).

Materials Millisecond timer
Photogates (2)
Meter stick
Pencil

Safety Precautions Wear chemical splash goggles and always follow laboratory safety rules while performing demonstrations.

Preparation Assemble the equipment. (See your physics department for the above equipment.) Most timer/photogate systems can work in two modes, a gate mode where the timer only runs when the beam in one of the photogates is blocked, and a start/stop mode, where the timer starts when the beam in one photogate is broken and stops when the beam in the other photogate is broken. This demonstration requires that both modes be used.

Demonstration **Part 1:** Configure the timer in the gate mode. Pass the pencil through the beam and record the time. A speed which will give a time of 5 milliseconds is adequate. The beam diameter is small, typically 2 mm. The concept here is that while the timer is running, the pencil must be somewhere inside that 2 mm region, which is a fairly precise position. Assuming a timer accuracy of ± 0.001 seconds allows us to calculate the uncertainty in the velocity. Typical calculations are as follows:

$$v = \text{distance/time}$$
$$= 0.2 \text{ cm beam width}/0.005 \text{ s}$$
$$= 40 \text{ cm/s}$$

Since the timer uncertainty is ± 0.001 seconds, this actually means that the velocity can be anything between 33 and 50 cm/s. (0.2 cm/0.006 s or 0.2 cm/0.004 s). This results in an uncertainty of about 20% in the velocity calculation.

Part 2: Configure the timer into the start/stop mode. Position the photogates one meter apart and run the pencil through both photogates. A time of 2 to 2.5 seconds is adequate. Typical calculations for this section are as follows:

$$v = \text{distance/time}$$
$$= 100 \text{ cm}/2.244 \text{ s}$$
$$= 44.56 \text{ cm/s}$$

The range of possible values at ± 0.001 seconds timer uncertainty are:

$$100 \text{ cm}/2.243 \text{ s} = 44.58 \text{ cm/s}$$
$$\text{to}$$
$$100 \text{ cm}/2.245 \text{ s} = 44.54 \text{ cm/s};$$

an uncertainty of only 0.04%.

We now have a relatively accurate velocity, but the pencil's position during this time can only be approximated as somewhere inside a 100 cm region. Thus students can see that if we have an accurate position, the velocity is uncertain and vice versa.

Disposal   None required.

Reference   John Koob, Queen of Peace High School, North Arlington, NJ.

Photocatalysis

The reaction between two gases is catalyzed using light from a photoflash.

Application | Catalysis • Photocatalysis • Gas Reactions • Explosion • Ozone Depletion

Theory | The reaction is $H_2 + Cl_2 \rightarrow 2\ HCl$. The reaction is initiated when a photon of light dissociates the Cl–Cl bond. Once the bond is dissociated, the reaction proceeds via a radical chain mechanism. The energy of the chlorine–chlorine bond is 242.44 kJ/mol.

The longest wavelength of light that will provide sufficient energy to dissociate this bond is about 493 nm. This wavelength lies in the greenish-blue region of the visible spectrum. (Hydrogen -b line is 486 nm). Therefore, light in the blue, violet and UV will work, while light in the red and yellow regions will not. This bond dissociation is similar to what occurs with chlorine in the upper atmosphere leading to ozone depletion. The relationship between wavelength and energy can be shown by fitting different color filters in front of the flash and determining when the transmitted light no longer has enough energy to catalyze the reaction.

Materials | 13×100 mm Test tubes (2)
Rubber stopper, 2-hole #00 (2)
Beral-type pipet, thin stem (4)

Glass delivery tubes, see diagram (2)
Potassium permanganate, $KMnO_4$,
Hydrogen chloride, conc. 12 M, HCl
Hydrogen chloride, 3 M, HCl
Zinc, mossy
Camera flash unit
250-mL Beaker filled 3/4 full of water
Piece of wood with a small headless nail imbedded (launching pad)

Safety Precautions | Hydrochloric acid is toxic by ingestion or inhalation, severely corrosive to skin and eyes. Potassium permanganate is a strong oxidizer and can explode upon heating and is a strong skin irritant. The volumes of chlorine being generated are very small, but chlorine is a respiratory irritant, and toxic by inhalation. Set up only in a well ventilated area.

Preparation | Cut stems on two Beral-type pipets to 1/4 inch. Fill beaker up 3/4 full with water. See diagram for set-up. Remove clear plastic lens from camera flash unit and replace with Saranwrap®.

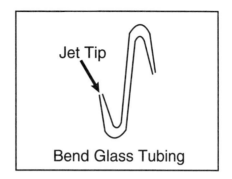

Jet Tip

Bend Glass Tubing

Demonstration

Fill the two pipets that have the cut stems completely with water. Insert the delivery tubes and the uncut pipets into the stoppers. To one test tube, add a few pieces of zinc. Fill one pipet with 3 M HCl. Insert the stopper assembly, and squeeze some of the HCl into the tube to begin hydrogen generation.

Allow a minute or two for the air to be excluded from the generator. then half-fill the two pipet bulbs by water displacement. Fill the other Beral-type pipet with concentrated HCl. Place about 1 to 2 grams of the permanganate crystals in the other test tube, then insert the stopper assembly. Squeeze some of the concentrated HCl from the dropper so that it contacts the permanganate in the bottom of the test tube and begins the generation of the chlorine. Again, allow a minute or two for the air to be expelled from the generator. Now, add chlorine gas from the delivery tip to the pipet that already contains the hydrogen. Leave a small amount of water in the neck of the bulbs to act as a seal and give some mass to act as a propellant. Place the stem over the nail on the launching pad. Hold the flash unit as close as you can to the pipet bulb and fire the flash. Repeat with the other pipet.

Disposal

The residue in the test tube may be flushed down the drain with excess water.

Reference

W. Rohr, EastChester High School, EastChester, NY.

Wave Generator

Demonstrate the relationships between wavelength and frequency when the speed of light is constant, $c = \lambda \upsilon$.

Application	Wave Properties • Speed of Light
Theory	Electromagnetic radiation travels at constant speed (velocity), c, and radiation is assumed to travel as waves. Waves have two major variable characteristics, wavelength and frequency. Speed = Frequency × Wavelength ($c = \lambda \upsilon$). Since speed is constant, frequency and wavelength are inversely related. As one gets larger, the other must get smaller.

Material

File folder, standard letter size	Marker, permanent transparency
Transparency sheet, clear overhead	Scissors
Masking tape, one-half inch wide	Overhead projector

Safety Precautions

Wear chemical splash goggles and always follow laboratory safety rules while performing demonstrations.

Preparation

Place strips of masking tape on the transparency leaving half-inch spaces between each. Run the tape the short, 8.5-inch direction. Color the first space between two strips of tape, red.

Open the file folder and lay it flat. On one side of it sketch two waves, one with a long wavelength and low frequency, the other with a short wavelength and high frequency. The first might be $\lambda = 1$ while the second might be $\lambda = 5$. Run the waves parallel to the length of the folder, the 11 inch direction, and keep the amplitude of both waves the same.

Now cut the waves with a sharp scissors from end to end, but do not cut all of the way through the ends of the folder. Cut the waves again about 3 mm apart from the first cut so light now passes through. This might take some practice. Fine scissors work best.

Demonstration

Discuss the concept to be demonstrated with the class and put the formula on the board. Place the file folder on the overhead, opened so the waves show on the screen. Discuss the differences in the two waves.

Now place the transparency under the folder so the red line shows through at one end of the waves. Slowly drag the transparency across the waves and watch the line of red light travel at constant velocity but make five sine waves at high frequency (short wavelength) and only one at low frequency (long wavelength). Repeat as often as necessary.

Disposal

Save the entire setup for next year.

Reference

George R. Hague, St. Mark's School, Dallas, TX.

Ionic and Molecular Solids

Differences between ionic and molecular solids are demonstrated using a conductivity apparatus.

Application | Bonding • Physical Properties • Conductivity • Electrolytes

Theory | Molecular solids and ionic solids show fundamental differences in behavior due to basic differences in the type of particle that makes up the solid and the type and strength of the forces that hold the crystal together. In a molecular solid, the particles that make up the unit crystal are covalently bonded molecules. Since all valence level electrons are paired, and valence shells are full, the only forces that can act to hold the crystal together are relatively weak interactions like London forces, or dipole–dipole interactions. For this reason, molecular solids are usually fairly soft and have relatively low melting points. Since these solids consist of molecules, with no net electric charge, they are non-conductors of electricity as solids, liquids, and solutions. Ionic solids are fundamentally different. The particles in the unit crystal are oppositely charged ions, which produce significantly larger forces of attraction. These solids generally have higher melting points. When this type of solid is melted, the ions are released from the crystal lattice, and become mobile. The pure liquid is therefore an excellent electrical conductor. Solutions of these solids are also strong electrolytes, since they dissociate completely as they dissolve, again producing mobile ions.

Materials | Sodium acetate, $CH_3CO_2Na \cdot 3H_2O$ — Paraffin
Sodium chloride, $NaCl$ — Conductivity apparatus
Sucrose, $C_{12}H_{22}O_{11}$ — 50-mL Crucible
Wash bottle with distilled or deionized water — 100-mL Beakers
High-temperature gas burner (Meker-type)

Safety Precautions | Sodium acetate is a skin, eye, and respiratory irritant. Wear chemical splash goggles and always follow laboratory safety rules while performing demonstrations.

Preparation | Put 5 to 10 grams of each solid into separate beakers and label.

Demonstration | Set up and plug in the conductivity apparatus. Show students that none of the solids are conductors. Transfer the sodium chloride to the crucible and heat the crucible strongly until the sodium chloride melts. Show that the melted material conducts. Clean the electrodes by rinsing with distilled water. Show students that distilled water will not conduct electricity. Make a sodium acetate solution and test the conductivity. Make a sucrose solution and test. Finally, melt the paraffin by heating gently and test its conductivity.

Disposal | The solids can be discarded in the trash and the solutions flushed down the drain with excess water.

Reference | Cotton, F. A., et al. *Chemistry, An Investigative Approach, Revised Edition;* Houghton Mifflin: Boston, 1980; p 382.

Viscosity

Viscosity is often discussed but cannot be appreciated until demonstrated.

Application

Organic Chemistry • Viscosity • Hydrogen Bonding • Polarity • Physical Properties

Theory

Sticky-gooeyness or viscosity is caused by many variables within the structures of substances. Included among these are the shape and size of the molecule, molecular weight, polarity of the molecule and presence of hydrogen bonding. If we assume the same temperature, these variables may be explored via our selection of substances to be tested. Relative viscosities of various liquids may be determined directly if similar objects are permitted to fall freely through a column of the liquids. Similarly, relative viscosities may be determined by allowing the liquids to flow freely from a narrow orifice.

Materials

Various organic liquids (e.g.):
  Alcohols
  Ethylene glycol
  Motor oil, Hexane
  Karo® syrup, Molasses
  Acetone, etc.
Beads of constant diameter or "cube-o-grams"

Water
Burets or long glass tubes
Culture tubes with screw caps
Food coloring (optional)
Beakers
Timer, clock with second hand

Safety Precautions

Treat all hydrocarbons and alcohols as flammable materials. Wear chemical splash goggles, chemical-resistant gloves and chemical-resistant apron. Always follow laboratory safety rules while performing demonstrations.

Preparation

Method A requires filling burets with the test liquids and mounting on ring stands. Coloring of liquids may be a wise means of making them visible since most are clear and colorless.

Method B uses culture tubes and requires advanced filling of the tubes and placing one of the beads or "cube-o-grams" in each tube. Fill the tubes completely and secure the caps tightly.

For either demo, line the burets or tubes in full view. Locate the timer so all may see it.

Demonstration

Method A: One buret may be emptied at a time and the times recorded to empty equal amounts, say 10 mL.

Method B: Each tube may be placed upside down and the time of fall of the bead noted for each liquid.

Alternatively, student volunteers may help to do all of the samples simultaneously.

Disposal

All liquids may be saved for future demonstrations. If they are not saved, choose the appropriate Flinn Suggested Disposal Method from the *Flinn Chemical Catalog/Reference Manual.*

Carbon–carbon double bonds are frequently refered to as unsaturated or polyunsaturated compounds, especially in advertisements for margarines and cooking oils.

Application | Organic Chemistry • Bonding • Consumer Chemistry

Theory | The reactivity of the double, unsaturated carbon–carbon bond is heightened due to the increased electron density around the bond. Electron-loving substances can attack this site readily and break the bond adding to the existing molecule at that site. The process is known as electrophilic addition.

For comparison a single bonded substance shows no reaction with the same reagent.

Materials

Test tubes, large	Hexane or other saturated hydrocarbon
Test tube rack	Cyclohexene or other unsaturated hydrocarbon
Bromine water	Salad oils

Safety Precautions | Hexane or other saturated hydrocarbons are flammable liquids and a dangerous fire risk. Bromine water is toxic by inhalation and ingestion. Wear chemical splash goggles, chemical-resistant gloves and a chemical-resistant apron.

Preparation | Bromine water may be purchased (Flinn BO166). It may also be prepared from pure bromine but this is discouraged for safety reasons.

Set up test tubes in a wire rack for visibility. Pour equal amounts, 20 mL usually works well, of hexane, cyclohexene and various salad oils or margarines into separate test tubes. Bacon fat also works well. Have a bottle of bromine water ready to use. If desired, a pipet or small graduated cylinder may be handy to assure approximately equal quantities of bromine water are added.

Demonstration | Place rack of test tubes in a highly visible position. Indicate which material is in each test tube. Add equal amounts of bromine water, 10 mL works well, to each substance announcing which substance is in the test tube each time.

Shake each test tube, pointing out the aqueous layer on the bottom and the disappearance of the orange color each time. Remember that if the color persists, double bonds are not present. Having the bottles of oils on the table adds some credibility to the demo.

Disposal | The brominated compounds are relatively safe in the small amounts generated and may be flushed of down the drain with excess water.

Excess organic hydrocarbons may be evaporated in small amounts in the hood, and nonvolatile edible oils may be flushed down the drain with excess water.

Excess bromine water can be disposed of according to Flinn Suggested Disposal Method 12a.

Intermolecular Attractions — A Sticky Subject

A quick-drying adhesive demonstrates intermolecular attractions.

Application | Intermolecular Forces • Bonding • Polymers • Adhesives

Theory | An adhesive is a substance that can hold materials together at their surface by maximizing the intermolecular attractions between the two surfaces. The earliest adhesives consisted of mixtures of flour paste and egg whites.

If two perfectly smooth surfaces are pressed together in a vacuum, the molecules on one surface will attract the molecules of the other surface. These intermolecular attractions will hold the surfaces together.

Ordinary surfaces are not smooth however, and few exist in vacuum. Most surfaces are full of microscopic ridges and valleys. Two surfaces which are to be bonded, however, can be coated with a substance that will fill these crevices. If the substance itself is made of atoms that hold on to each other tightly, the coated surfaces can bond.

Epoxies and glues are polymer molecules that are held together with strong covalent bonds and have branches that are polar. These polar branches can bind with the molecule of other similar molecules. An epoxy consists of two components: a prepolymer and a curing agent. An epoxy prepolymer combines chemically with a curing agent to form an interlocking polymer. The -OH groups in the final polymer are so strongly attracted to the surface to which the glue is applied that stress will fracture the polymer before the polymer breaks from the surface.

Epoxy Resin

Materials	5-minute Epoxy Wooden stirrer Coffee mug with broken handle or similar item
Safety Precautions	Follow safety precautions on package of epoxy. Wear chemical splash goggles, chemical-resistant gloves and a chemical-resistant apron.
Preparation	Glue two surfaces using epoxy as the adhesive according to the instructions on the packaging. Allow to set for 24 hours. The next day try to break the adhesion. Notice that the breakage will occur in the adhesive—both surfaces of the bond should still be coated with dry adhesive.
Disposal	The solids can be disposed of in the trash.
Reference	Wilbraham, A., et al. *Chemistry;* Addison Wesley: Menlo Park, CA, 1987; pp 341–342.

Polar/Nonpolar Liquids

Show the behavior of polar and non-polar liquids in the presence of an electrical charge.

Application Chemical Bonding • Physical Properties • Polarity

Theory The water molecule is bent, and contains two polar covalent hydrogen–oxygen bonds. The molecule is therefore polar, slightly negative at the oxygen end and slightly positive at the hydrogen end. The molecule will be attracted to a charged object. The polarity of water accounts for its liquid state at room temperature, its lower density as ice, its ability to dissolve ions, and its tendency to form ions, H^+ and OH^-. The hexane molecule has no polarity, and is not attracted.

Materials Buret (2)
250-mL Beakers (2)
Water
Hexane
Plastic or rubber rod
Fur or wool

Safety Precautions Hexane is a flammable liquid, a dangerous fire risk and a respiratory irritant. Avoid open flames or hot surfaces. Wear chemical splash goggles, chemical-resistant gloves and a chemical-resistant apron.

Demonstration Fill one buret with water, the other with hexane. Charge the plastic or rubber rod by rubbing it briskly with the fur or wool. A plastic ruler rubbed through your hair also works well, and you can say something about your "magnetic" personality. Open the stopcock of the water buret until you get a fine unbroken stream, and hold the charged rod near it. Observe that the stream is attracted to it. Repeat the procedure with hexane, the stream will be unaffected.

Disposal Hexanes can be disposed of by evaporation in a fume hood.

Reference Summerlin, L., et al. *Chemical Demonstrations;* American Chemical Society: Washington, DC, 1988; Vol. 2, p 91.

Polar/Nonpolar Disks

The attraction of polar molecules to polar solvents and non-polar molecules to non-polar solvents is clearly shown.

Application | Bonding • Intermolecular Forces • Polarity

Theory | Polar molecules are best attracted to polar solvents, while non-polar molecules are best attracted to non-polar solvents. Cellulose is a polar substance, while graphite is non-polar.

Materials | 250-mL Erlenmeyer flask
Solid rubber stopper to fit
Water
Non-polar solvent (hexane, lighter fluid, naphtha)
Pencil lead, #2 or softer
Index card
Hole punch

Safety Precautions | Hexane and naphtha are flammable, dangerous fire risks, and respiratory irritants. Avoid open flames or hot surfaces. Wear chemical splash goggles, chemical-resistant gloves and a chemical-resistant apron.

Preparation | Make the polar/non-polar disks by blackening one side of the index card with the pencil, covering the surface thoroughly. Punch out a dozen or so disks with a hole punch.

Demonstration | Place equal volumes of water and the non-polar substance into the flask. To show students which layer is organic (non-polar), take a few drops from each layer and add to water in a test tube and/or add a few drops of food coloring. Add the disks to the flask and stopper. Shake or swirl the flask to get the disks to the interface between the two layers. The disks will orient themselves according to their polarity. Students will be able to see that paper (cellulose) is polar while graphite (containing carbon–carbon bonds) is non-polar.

Disposal | Separate the organic layer from the aqueous layer. Dispose of the organic substance by evaporation in a hood.

The disks can be separated by filtration and discarded in the trash.

Reference | Woodrow Wilson Chem 11 Institute.

Metallic Bonding

A homemade overhead projector device is used to simulate changes that effect metallic bonding.

Application	Bonding • Metals
Theory	The crystalline structure of metallic solids is inherently different from other crystalline solids. Positions in the unit crystal are occupied by metal atoms, but their valence electrons are delocalized. That is, the electrons are not bound to any specific atom, but are free to move throughout the solid. The term "Electron Gas" has sometimes been used to describe this. The ability of electrons to move is responsible for the excellent thermal and electrical conductivity of most metals.
	The packing of atoms in a metallic crystal is usually closer than in any other type of solid.

Materials

For construction:
Copper shot (50 mL)
Plexiglas®, $20 \times 30 \times 1$ cm (2)
Plexiglas, $1 \times 30 \times 1$ cm (2)
Plexiglas, $1 \times 18 \times 1$ cm (2)
Methylene chloride, CH_2Cl_2
Acrylic plastic cement
Glass dropper
Router, with straight trimmer bit (optional)

For demonstration:
Hair pins (3)
Tongs
Bunsen burner
250-mL Beaker
Overhead projector

Safety Precautions

When working with power hand tools always wear eye protection. Methylene chloride will dissolve many plastics and can be a narcotic in high concentrations. Wear chemical splash goggles and always follow laboratory safety rules while performing demonstrations.

Preparation

Assemble the materials listed previously. Align the four small pieces along the edge of one of the Plexiglas sheets. Use a few pieces of masking tape to hold the pieces in position temporarily. Using a glass dropper, carefully apply a stream of methylene chloride into the space between the pieces of plastic. Capillary action should make the solvent flow easily between the pieces. As the solvent is added, be certain that it does not come into contact with the masking tape, as this will cause the solvent to move into the center of the frame—leaving permanent streaking marks.

It is best to remove the tape as the solvent is added. Next, pour the copper shot into the plastic frame and cover with the second piece of plastic. Affix this piece in the same manner using the methylene chloride solvent. The edge of the entire viewer may be trimmed using a router with a straight trimmer bit (optional). Acrylic plastic cement can also be used instead of methylene chloride to assemble the viewer.

Demonstration	**Regular metallic crystals**
Take a bobby pin and heat it in a Bunsen burner until it is glowing hot and then allow it to cool slowly undisturbed. Try bending the cooled pin. It should bend easily. Discuss the formation of metallic crystals and the regular patterns they normally form. The metallic bond viewer may be use to simulate the formation of metallic bonds. To do this, first lay the viewer on a flat surface and then slowly tilt it to allow the spheres to align themselves in a regular pattern at one end. Move the viewer to the overhead projector—being careful not to disturb the positions of the "atoms". You may wish to discuss the properties associated with metals and how this regular pattern contributes to these properties.

Tempering a metal
Take another bobby pin and heat it in the Bunsen burner. Once the pin is red-hot, quickly immerse it in a beaker of cold water to temper it. Remove the pin and bend it. It should break. Discuss the effect the quick cooling has on the formation of the metallic crystal. The metallic bond viewer may be used to simulate what occurred when the metal was cooled quickly. To do this, first gently shake the viewer to reposition the spheres and then quickly tilt it to allow the spheres to fall in a random pattern. Move the viewer to the overhead projector— being careful not to disturb the positions of the "atoms". You may wish to discuss the advantages and disadvantages of tempering a metal.

Annealing a metal
Take a third bobby pin and heat it in the Bunsen burner. As before, once the pin is red-hot immerse it in a beaker of cold water in order to temper it. Remove the pin and then heat it gently in the Bunsen burner. As the pin is heated it should develop a bluish color. The color change is an indicator that the metal is annealed and heating should cease. The metallic bond viewer may be used to simulate the annealing process by tapping the side of the viewer allowing some of the "atoms" to reposition themselves. |

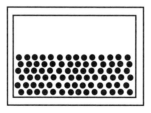 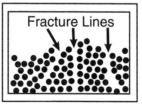 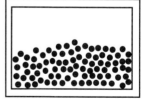

Regular Metallic Crystal	Tempered Metallic Crystal	Annealed Metallic Crystal

Disposal	None required.
Reference	Institute for Chemical Education; University of Wisconsin—Madison, Summer, 1989.

Alchemist's Gold

A copper penny is placed in a solution resulting in the penny turning silver and then gold after it is heated.

Application | Alchemy • Alloys

Theory | Prior to the times of Lavosier of the 1700's, chemists—who were known as alchemists were generally preoccupied with finding the means to turn matter into gold. Alchemists spent years developing techniques and trickery that made their audiences believe that they had the ability of turning lead, and other substances into gold. One such trick involved filling a bored-out metal stirring rod with gold dust. The tip of the rod was then sealed with wax in order to contain the dust and to keep it from being seen by others. To prove himself as a master alchemist, the charlatan would stir a heated, empty crucible with this rod and (as the wax melted) the vessel would slowly fill with molten gold. Although alchemists were measured by the "success" of their trickery, their less-than-systematic research played an important contribution to laying the foundation for chemists like Lavosier and others to build upon. It was the alchemists that discovered and developed the various techniques of chemical purification such as fractional distillation and sublimation.

When the penny is heated in a solution of sodium hydroxide and in the presence of zinc powder, atoms of zinc which have gone into solution migrate towards the penny and deposit a coating of zinc onto the copper. This process is known as wet-chemical plating, as opposed to electrochemical plating. The coating of zinc gives the penny an appearance of silver. If the "silver" penny is heated gently, the zinc on the surface mixes with the outer layers of copper atoms of the penny producing an alloy which looks like gold. In making this alloy, the atoms must actually exchange places to facilitate mixing—this is accomplished by adding heat to cause the natural vibrational motion of the copper and zinc atoms to turn into fluid motion.

Materials | Copper pennies (Use pennies dated 1982 and earlier.)
Sodium hydroxide, 6 M, NaOH (100 mL)
400-mL Ceramic casserole or evaporating dish
Zinc, powder or granular (5 g)
Glass stirring rod
Metal tongs
400-mL Beaker
Hot plate
Bunsen burner
Soft cloth

Safety Precautions

Sodium hydroxide solutions are corrosive, skin burns are possible, very dangerous to eyes. Heat the sodium hydroxide gently to prevent spattering. Use a hot plate to heat this solution and do not allow the solution to boil. Wear chemical splash goggles, chemical-resistant gloves, a chemical-resistant apron and conduct the demonstration under a fume hood or in a well-ventilated area. Zinc dust can be a dangerous fire risk and may form explosive mixtures with air. Do not use post-1982 pennies as they contain a core of zinc that may lead to a violent reaction with the sodium hydroxide.

Preparation

Purchase or prepare 6 M NaOH. Place a 250-mL beaker into a cold water bath. Slowly dissolve 24 g sodium hydroxide in 100 mL water. Be certain to dissolve the sodium hydroxide a little at a time as the dissolving process is highly exothermic.

Demonstration

Pour the sodium hydroxide solution into a ceramic casserole or large evaporating dish. Add 5 g zinc powder to the solution and proceed to heat on a hot plate. Do not boil!

Copper into "Silver": Place a penny or two into the zinc-sodium hydroxide mixture. Stir the contents of the casserole while continuing to heat for about two minutes until the penny develops a silver appearance. Remove the penny with metallic tongs and dip it in water a few times to dilute any adhering solution. The penny may be dried and polished with a soft cloth to develop a sheen.

"Silver" into "Gold": Using tongs, take one of the silver pennies and pass it back and forth through the flame of a Bunsen burner. As the penny is heated it will develop the appearance of gold.

Disposal

If the residual zinc is a dust, it is a fire risk and the sodium hydroxide on the zinc must be removed. The best way to remove the dust and sodium hydroxide from the zinc is to rinse the zinc with copious quantities of water. (20 minutes minimum)

Do not discard the zinc if you have not followed the above process. Zinc can be reused. Any leftover sodium hydroxide solution can be neutralized and rinsed down the drain with excess water.

Reference

Institute for Chemical Education, University of Wisconsin—Madison, Summer, 1989.

Parrington, J. R. *A Short History of Chemistry;* MacMillan: London, 1937.

Nonadditivity of Volumes 1 + 1 < 2

When two substances form a solution, their volumes are not necessarily additive.

Application | Solutions • Density • Hydrogen Bonding

Theory | The process of forming a solution initially involves the particles of one substance filling in the spaces between the particles of another substance, once this space is filled, the volume of the combining mixture begins to increase.

As the ethanol fills the spaces between the water molecules, the total volume of the mixture must decrease. One would expect the bubble formed to be a vacuum. In fact it is a partial vacuum filled with water and ethanol vapors. At the end of the demonstration, quietly and slowly remove the stopper from one end. Note the suction of air into the tube.

Materials | Glass tube or eudiometer, 1 meter long
Rubber stoppers (2)
Water (50 mL)
Green food coloring
Ethanol, C_2H_5OH (50 mL)

Safety Precautions | Ethanol is flammable and a dangerous fire risk—keep away from open flame. Wear chemical splash goggles, chemical-resistant gloves and a chemical-resistant apron.

Demonstration | Stopper one end of a 1 meter long glass tube. Fill the tube half way with colored water (green works well for contrast). Carefully, trying not to mix, add ethanol until the tube is completely filled. Stopper the other end of the tube being certain that no air bubbles remain. Have students note that the tube contains no air. You may also wish to discuss the fact that the alcohol apparently floats in water (it's less dense).

Begin inverting the tube slowly to cause the water and ethanol to mix. Periodically stop and allow students to make observations. In time in should be evident that a bubble is growing in the tube. Discuss the contents of this bubble and how it demonstrates nonadditivity of volumes.

Disposal | Solutions can be flushed down the drain with excess water.

Water Delivery

Water exhibits both adhesive and cohesive properties while traveling along a string.

Application | Intermolecular Forces • Capillary Action • Hydrogen Bonding

Theory | This activity shows the adhesive and cohesive forces that are at work in ordinary water. A cotton string soaked in water shows adhesion while the water on the wet string demonstrates the cohesive properties by clinging to other water molecules.

Materials | Tap water
Cotton string
250-mL Beakers (2)

Safety Precautions | Wear chemical splash goggles and always follow laboratory safety rules while performing demonstrations.

Preparation | Cut a piece of string about 50 cm in length. Soak the string in water until saturated. 30 minutes is recommended as a minimum.

Demonstration | Fill one beaker about 3/4 full with water. Have an assistant hold one end of the string over the empty beaker. Stretch the string taut at approximately a 30 degree angle and carefully pour the water from the beaker down the string. Continue until the beaker is completely empty. Once the technique has been mastered, you can increase the distance between the two beakers. This makes an excellent contest at a science fair. Students have been known to fill beakers as far apart as 30 meters!

Disposal | None required.

Reference | Liem, T. *Invitations to Science Inquiry,* 2nd ed.; Science Inquiry: China Hills, CA, 1989; p 110.

Optical Rotation of Sugars

Optical rotation of sugars is to be measured using an overhead projector.

Application | Organic Chemistry • Isomers

Theory | Fructose, the primary component of corn syrup, is an optically active compound that will rotate the plane of polarized light.

Materials | Overhead projector
Polarizing film, Flinn AP8913 (2)
250-mL Beaker
Karo™ syrup (colorless, not the dark!)
Protractor

Safety Precautions | Wear chemical splash goggles and always follow laboratory safety rules while performing demonstrations.

Demonstration | Place a sheet of polarizing film on the stage of an overhead projector and then place a 250-mL beaker on top of the film. Place another sheet of polarizing film on top of the beaker. Rotate the top film to obtain the maximum reduction of light intensity through the film.

Pour the Karo™ syrup into the beaker and note the increased light intensity due to the light rotation by the sugar in the syrup. Rotate the top sheet until the light is again at a minimum. Use the protractor to measure the angle of optical rotation. This activity can then be extended to different sugars and different concentrations.

Disposal | The Karo™ syrup can be flushed down the drain with excess water.

Reference | Michael Bannon, Brentwood High School, Brentwood, NY, at Woodrow Wilson Chem 4 Institute.

Harnessing the Nucleus — Ping-Pong Chain Reaction

Mousetraps setting each other off is used as an analogy to understand the concept of a nuclear chain reaction.

Application
Chain Reactions • Nuclear Chemistry • Fission

Theory
Commercial nuclear power plants and the most common forms of nuclear weaponry depend on the process of nuclear fission for their operation. Fission involves splitting heavy nuclei into other lighter nuclei. Uranium–235 is commonly used for nuclear fission and on average, produces 2.4 neutrons from every fission. If one fission produces 2 neutrons, these 2 neutrons each cause two more fissions and the resulting 4 neutrons thereby released can produce four more fissions, and so forth. The number of fissions and the energy released quickly escalates. If left uncontrolled, the reactions are explosive. Reactions that multiply in this fashion are called chain reactions.

Materials
Mousetraps (50)
Ping-Pong® balls or corks (100)

Safety Precautions
Wear chemical splash goggles and always follow laboratory safety rules while performing demonstrations.

Demonstration
Set fifty mouse traps—each with two Ping-Pong balls lying on the spring. Throw one Ping-Pong ball at the group of mousetraps. The entire collection of traps should set off within seconds of throwing the first ball.

The reaction can be contained by placing a baby crib screen over the "reactor".

Disposal
None required.

Swinging Electrons

Paramagnetic properties of atoms are explained by their electron configurations.

Application | Electron Configurations • Paramagnetism • Orbitals

Theory | Some compounds have valence shells that do not conform to the octet rule of eight. Certain molecules, having an even number of electrons, may have some unpaired electrons. As an example, compounds of boron have fewer than four pairs of electrons around the central atom. Compounds of the elements in groups 13, 15, 16 and 17 have more than four pairs of electrons around the central atom.

Zinc and calcium ions have completely filled s and p orbitals and zinc has completely filled d orbitals. Since there are no unpaired electrons in these ions, they are diamagnetic. Copper has nine electrons in its d orbitals, thus one unpaired electron. Copper is paramagnetic and is attracted to a magnet. Manganese is also paramagnetic since it has five unpaired electrons—one in each of the five orbitals.

Electron configurations of select ions:

$$Ca^{2+} \quad 1s^2 2s^2 2p^6 3s^2 3p^6 \text{ (diamagnetic)}$$

$$Zn^{2+} \quad 1s^2 2s^2 2p^6 3s^2 3p^6 4s^0 3d^{10} \text{ (diamagnetic)}$$

$$Cu^{2+} \quad 1s^2 2s^2 2p^6 3s^2 3p^6 4s^0 3d^9 \text{ (paramagnetic)}$$

$$Mn^{2+} \quad 1s^2 2s^2 2p^6 3s^2 3p^6 4s^0 3d^5 \text{ (most paramagnetic)}$$

Materials | Test tubes (8)   Thread
Calcium Sulfate, $CaSO_4$ Ring stand with clamp (2)
Manganese Sulfate, $MnSO_4$ Horizontal bar
Cupric Sulfate, $CuSO_4$ Powerful magnet
Zinc Sulfate, $ZnSO_4$

Safety Precautions | Cupric sulfate is a skin and respiratory irritant; toxic by ingestion and inhalation. Zinc sulfate is a skin and mucous membrane irritant. Manganese sulfate may be a tissue irritant. Wear chemical splash goggles, chemical-resistant gloves and a chemical-resistant apron.

Preparation | Prepare saturated solutions (see page S) of all four sulfates, place into four different test tubes. Place each metal sulfate (solid form) into a different test tube. Label test tubes.

Demonstration | Suspend the eight test tubes from a horizontal bar. Bring a magnet close to each of the test tubes. The test tubes containing manganese and copper will be attracted to the magnet. The test tubes containing the solid material will show a greater effect.

Disposal | Save the test tubes from year to year.

Chapter 11

Periodicity

Introducing the Periodic Table with Sodium

Sodium metal is used as a reference point in analyzing the relative reactivities of five metals in the introduction to periodicity.

Application | Periodicity • Reactivity • Physical Properties • Observation

Theory | In the early and mid-1800's it became apparent to many that there may be some benefit in determining if there existed any patterns in the properties of the known elements of the time. At this time there were about 60 known elements. Many scientists including Newlands, Meyer and Mendeleev spent much of their time developing an organizational scheme of the known elements. In 1817, Johann Wolfgang Döbereiner noticed that in certain groups of three elements, for example Ca, Sr and Ba, the atomic weight of the middle element was the approximate average of the other two. This was known as Döbereiner's Triad Theory. Other organizational schemes and tables followed, including Odling's Table of Elements (1865), Newlands' Table of Atomic Numbers (1865), Meyer's unpublished imperfect table (1868) and most noteworthy and convincing: The Periodic Table of Elements first presented by Dmitri Mendeleev (1869). This demonstration simulates the type of investigations conducted by these famous scientists in their development of one of the most impressive schemes of organization in history. Mendeleev's table is said to be impressive because his table of 1871 predicted and organized elements yet to be discovered. Mendeleev's predictions were near perfect.

Materials | Lithium metal, Li
Sodium metal, Na
Potassium metal, K
Calcium metal turnings or pieces, Ca
Magnesium metal ribbon, Mg
Petri or evaporating dishes (5)
250-mL Beakers (5)
Plexiglas®, (10 × 10 × .5 cm)
Tongs
Scalpel or knife
Safety shield

Safety Precautions | Alkali metals react violently with water to produce caustic hydroxides, hydrogen gas and heat. Enough heat can be produced to cause the hydrogen to ignite and explode spontaneously. Only react small quantities of these metals. Do not handle alkali metals directly. Always cover reaction vessel with a shatterproof cover. Wear chemical splash goggles, chemical-resistant gloves and a chemical-resistant apron.

Preparation | Prepare small pieces of lithium, sodium, and potassium metals. Flinn Scientific, Inc. sells small quantities (1 to 2.5 g) suitable for demonstrations.

Demonstration	Remove a small piece ($0.5 \times 0.5 \times 0.5$ cm) of each metal and observe the color, degree of shininess, hardness and malleability of each metal. The metals should be placed into a container, such as a Petri or evaporating dish. List the properties on a chalkboard and discuss which element appears the shiniest, softest, etc. You may wish to create a scale of shininess or hardness. Estimate the density of each metal. Scrape the oxide coating from each of the metals and observe their color. Notice that the lithium, sodium and potassium quickly develop a new oxide coating. As the properties are listed, have the class order the elements from softest to hardest or shiniest to least shiny.

Have students decide if the five metals can be organized into categories. Ultimately it is expected that students will place the metals into two categories: those metals that are soft and develop an oxide coating quickly and those that are harder (less soft) and do not develop an oxide coating. Have students name these categories—perhaps, soft metals and hard metals.

Fill five beakers half full of water. With a piece of Plexiglas (to serve as a lid) in one hand, quickly drop a small piece of sodium into the first beaker. Immediately cover the beaker with the plastic lid. As the sodium reacts it will melt from the heat and produce hydrogen gas which should ignite and possibly produce a small explosion which is easily contained in this setup. Repeat this procedure with each of the metals, always comparing the reactivity with respect to one another. You should expect that potassium will be the most reactive followed by sodium, lithium, calcium and finally magnesium. Magnesium is not expected to react.

When all the data is collected, begin comparing degrees of reactivity and see if there is a correlation between reactivity and shininess, reactivity and softness, etc. Have students make comparisons between the two categories that they previously established. Is there a relationship between metals in one group and metals in the other group?

Disposal

Any remaining metals should be saved for future use.

Residual solutions can be disposed of according to Flinn Suggested Disposal Method #10.

Reference

Parrington, J. R. *A Short History of Chemistry;* MacMillan: London, 1937.

Periodicity of Group II Metals

Investigate the trends in solubilities of the alkaline earth metal cations.

Application   Periodicity • Solubility • Precipitation • Qualitative Analysis

Theory   Alkaline earth metals occupy the second column or group in the periodic table. They form oxides and/or peroxides with properties that are similar to the alkali metals of group I. Their hydroxides, carbonates, sulfates, chromates and oxalates vary in solubility.

Materials   Ammonium oxalate, 0.2 M, $(NH_4)_2C_2O_4$ (100 mL)
Magnesium nitrate, 0.2 M, $Mg(NO_3)_2$ (100 mL)
Potassium chromate, 0.5 M, $K_2Cr_2O_4$ (100 mL)
Ammonium sulfate, 1 M, $(NH_4)_2SO_4$ (100 mL)
Strontium nitrate, 0.1 M, $Sr(NO_3)_2$ (100 mL)
Barium nitrate, 0.1 M, $Ba(NO_3)_2$ (100 mL)
Calcium nitrate, 0.1 M, $Ca(NO_3)_2$ (100 mL)
Ammonia, 6 M, (NH_4OH) (100 mL)
Ammonium carbonate, 2 M, $(NH_4)_2CO_3$
24-well Micro plate
Overhead projector
Eye droppers

Safety Precautions   Ammonia is toxic by ingestion and inhalation of both the vapor and liquid. It is very irritating to eyes and respiratory tract, use a fume hood to prepare solution. Nitrates are strong oxidants and a potential fire risk when in contact with organic material. Potassium chromate is corrosive to skin, eyes and respiratory tract. Strontium and barium compounds are toxic by ingestion. Oxalates are toxic by inhalation and ingestion. Wear chemical splash goggles, chemical-resistant gloves and a chemical-resistant apron—provide good ventilation during demonstration.

Preparation   Prepare solutions by dissolving the following materials and quantity in distilled water and diluting to a volume of 100 mL with distilled water:

0.2 M $(NH_4)_2C_2O_4$, 2.8 g	1 M $(NH_4)_2SO_4$, 13.2 g
0.2 M $Mg(NO_3)_2$, 5.1 g	0.1 M $Ba(NO_3)_2$, 2.6 g
0.5 M $K_2Cr_2O_4$, 9.7 g	0.1 M $Ca(NO_3)_2$, 2.4 g

2 M $(NH_4)_2CO_3$ with NH_3, dilute 19.2 g of $(NH_4)_2CO_3$ and 8 mL of 15 M NH_3(aq) to a volume of 100 mL with distilled or deionized water.

6 M Ammonia: Add 40 mL concentrate reagent to sufficient water to make 100 mL of solution.

Demonstration

Place the 24-well plate onto the stage of the overhead projector, and turn on the projector. Place 1 to 2 mL of magnesium nitrate solution into 5 wells in a horizontal row. You might want to use a calibrated eyedropper. Do the same with calcium, strontium, and barium nitrates in succeeding horizontal rows. Now add equal volumes of the test reagents to the wells in vertical rows. Have students note how the patterns of precipitate formation occur. The reaction with aqueous ammonia might be difficult to see, since it forms a suspension versus a true precipitate.

Disposal

Barium compounds and chromates should be disposed of by Flinn Suggested Disposal Methods #27h and #12a, respectively. All other solutions can be flushed down the drain with excess water.

Reference

Metcalfe, H. C., et al. *Exercises and Experiments in Modern Chemistry;* Holt, Rinehart, Winston: New York, 1986.

Reactions of Halogens

Demonstrate periodicity using the halogen family.

Application Periodicity • Halogens • Redox • Replacement Reactions

Theory Periodicity is a basic concept in chemistry. The members of a chemical family have different properties that vary as you proceed through a family, either up or down the chart.

In the halogen family, those elements nearer the top of the chart will replace those below. Thus the activity of the members of this family is, from most to least reactive: fluorine, chlorine, bromine and iodine.

A typical halogen replacement reaction may be represented as follows:

$$Cl_2 + 2NaBr \rightarrow Br_2 + 2NaCl$$

Materials
Laundry bleach, NaOCl	Hexanes
Sodium bromide, 0.1 M, NaBr	Large test tubes (4)
Sodium iodide, 0.1 M, NaI	Test tube rack
Sodium chloride, 0.1 M, NaCl	Light box if available

Safety Precautions Bleach, sodium hypochlorite solution, is a corrosive liquid, causes skin burns and evolves chlorine when heated or reacted with an acid. Sodium bromide, sodium iodide, sodium hypochlorite and the products from the reaction, bromine and iodine, are toxic by ingestion or inhalation. Hexanes are very flammable and may be irritating to the respiratory tract. Wear chemical splash goggles, chemical-resistant gloves and a chemical-resistant apron.

Preparation Prepare 0.1 M solutions of sodium chloride, sodium bromide and sodium iodide. Place 10 to 20 mL of the bleach, chloride, iodide and bromide solutions into four large test tubes in the rack on a light box.

Demonstration Briefly discuss periodicity. Note appearance of each solution and record. Add 10 to 20 mL of bleach to each tube. Note the changes that occur. Add 5 mL of hexanes to each tube and shake vigorously. Note the orange color in the bromide tube and the pinkish-purple color in the iodide tube. These represent the respective elements replaced from the ionic solutions. Note that the chloride solution does not change.

Optional: Set up another set of test tubes and this time add 10 to 20 mL of bromine water instead. Note that only the iodine tube changes. The color in the other tubes and the bromine tube is due to the bromine added.

Disposal Aqueous solutions may be flushed down the drain with excess water. Hexanes may be collected and evaporated in a fume hood.

Reference Summerlin, L., et al. *Chemical Demonstrations;* American Chemical Society: Washington, DC, 1988; Vol. 2, p 60.

Limewater Reaction Periodicity

Demonstrate that elements in the same family show similar reactions.

Application | Periodicity • Precipitation • Qualitative Analysis

Theory | Limewater, a saturated solution of calcium hydroxide, provides a traditional test for the presence of carbon dioxide. It turns cloudy in the presence of CO_2 due to the reaction:

$$Ca^{2+}(aq) + 2\ OH^-(aq) + CO_2(g) \rightarrow CaCO_3(s) + H_2O(l)$$

Similar reactions occur with hydroxides of the other elements of group II, and can be used to demonstrate this aspect of periodicity.

Materials | Limewater solution, saturated solution, $Ca(OH)_2$
Strontium hydroxide, saturated solution, $Sr(OH)_2$
Barium hydroxide, saturated solution, $Ba(OH)_2$
Magnesium hydroxide, saturated solution, $Mg(OH)_2$
Soda straw
Filter funnel
Filter paper disks
150-mL Beaker

Safety Precautions | Solutions are all strongly alkaline and can irritate skin and eyes. Barium compounds are toxic by ingestion. Wear chemical splash goggles, chemical-resistant gloves and a chemical-resistant apron.

Preparation | Prepare and filter saturated solutions (see page S) or purchase ready-made solutions from Flinn Scientific. If the solutions have a cloudy appearance, filter them just before use.

Demonstration | Pour about 30 mL of limewater into a 150-mL beaker. Blow through the straw into the solution. The cloudiness that results is caused by the precipitation of calcium carbonate. Repeat the procedure with the other solutions. Note whether the cloudiness occurs faster or slower. All solutions will produce the precipitate.

Disposal | Barium hydroxide can be disposed of by Flinn Suggested Disposal Method #27h and all the alkaline solutions neutralized according to Flinn Suggested Disposal Method #10 before flushing down the drain.

Reference | Metcalfe, H. C., et. al. *Exercises and Experiments in Modern Chemistry;* Holt, Rinehart, Winston: New York, 1986; p 235.

Electrovalent Bonding

Three different stoichiometric volumes of hydrogen gas are produced from metals of different charge.

Application	Electrovalence • Stoichiometry • Single Replacement Reactions • Gases
Theory	Anions and cations have opposite charges and attract one another by electrostatic forces. The forces of attraction that bind charged ions together are called ionic bonds. The total anion charge must be balanced by the total cation charge.

The reaction of metals with hydrochloric acid produces metal chlorides and hydrogen gas.

Magnesium will produce twice the volume of hydrogen gas than the sodium because magnesium can undergo a double oxidation to Mg^{+2}.

$$Na + HCl \rightarrow NaCl + \frac{1}{2} H_2$$

$$Mg + 2HCl \rightarrow MgCl_2 + H_2$$

These different amounts were produced because magnesium has twice the charge of sodium—therefore each magnesium atom must react with two HCl molecules to acquire two chlorine atoms. An aluminum–acid reaction will generate three times the amount of hydrogen gas as the sodium–acid reaction. Each aluminum atom reacts with three HCl molecules to acquire three chlorine atoms.

$$Al + 3HCl \rightarrow AlCl_3 + \frac{3}{2} H_2$$

Materials

Sodium, Na (23 mg)
Magnesium, Mg (24 mg)
Aluminum, Al (27 mg)
250-mL Volumetric flasks or boiling flasks (3)
Balloons (3)
Paper towels
Spatulas
Hydrochloric acid, 0.1 M, HCl
Hydrochloric acid, 3M, HCl

Safety Precautions

Sodium is a flammable, corrosive solid. Do not expose to heat or flame. Keep water and aqueous solutions away from sodium. Sodium must be stored under anhydrous mineral oil or kerosene. The reaction of sodium and acid is extremely volatile. Hydrogen gas is explosive. All metallic samples should be as clean as possible. As a precaution, volumetric flasks are used in this demonstration to prevent the reactants from coming into contact with the balloon once the reaction has started. Aluminum and magnesium powders are flammable and can form explosive mixtures in air. Hydrochloric acid is highly toxic by ingestion or inhalation, severly corrosive to skin and eyes. Wear chemical splash goggles, chemical-resistant gloves and a chemical-resistant apron.

Preparation	Weigh out equal molar quantities of the 3 metals. Suggested amount is 0.23 mg Na, 0.24 mg Mg, and 0.27 mg Al. Prepare (see page A) or purchase acid solutions.
Demonstration	Place about 100 mL 3M hydrochloric acid into the first two flasks. Place 100 mL of 0.1 M HCl into the flask into which the sodium metal will be added. Wipe off as much oil as possible from the sodium sample. Place the samples in separate balloons. Secure the balloons over the flasks. Allow the metals to fall into the acid. The metals will react immediately to produce hydrogen gas which is trapped in the balloons.
Disposal	All solutions can be flushed down the drain with excess water.

Chapter 12

Solutions and Colloids

Solutions of Moles

Understanding molarity is enhanced when the moles of solution can be seen.

Application | Solutions • Molarity • Moles

Theory | Molarity is the most important unit of concentration in chemistry. Molarity is the number of moles of solute dissolved in 1 liter of solution. In this demonstration, the solute is represented by stuffed moles (the animal). Moles are introduced into a 2-liter soda bottle. In turn students determine the concentration of the "solution" from the number of moles "dissolved" into the 2-liter bottle.

Materials | Stuffed moles (3 or more whole, 2 to 3 halves)
2-liter Soda bottle
1-liter Beaker

Safety Precautions | Wear chemical splash goggles and always follow laboratory safety rules while performing demonstrations.

Preparation | Moles need to be sewn prior to presentation. In addition to the "whole" moles, it is useful to sew a few moles that are made from two halves held together with Velcro®. The Velcro halves may be pulled apart resulting in "half moles". (See pattern and remember the words "extra credit"!)

Cut part way around the top of a soda bottle so it can be opened—leave enough for a hinge.

Demonstration | Introduce the concept of molarity:

$$\text{Molarity (M)} = \frac{\text{number of moles of solute}}{\text{number of liters of solution}}$$

Place one mole into a 1-liter beaker and explain that the solution has a concentration of 1 mole per liter. Continue placing more moles into the beaker, pausing with each to determine the solution concentration.

Introduce the moles into a 2-liter soda bottle and repeat the above presentation.

Introduce the half moles as fractions of moles in solution. Determine the concentration for each combination.

Disposal | Keep moles for next year.

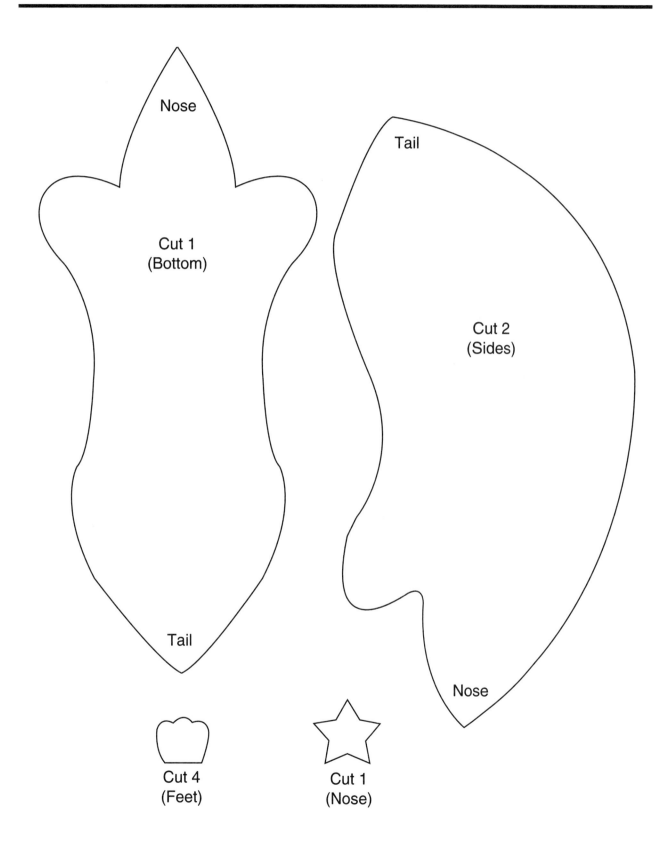

Nose

Cut 1
(Bottom)

Tail

Tail

Cut 2
(Sides)

Nose

Cut 4
(Feet)

Cut 1
(Nose)

Nonadditivity of Volumes 1 + 1 > 2

Addition of one mole of acid to a mole of base results in the formation of water and a volume expansion.

Application	Acids and Bases • Volume • Stoichiometry
Theory	The reaction of a strong acid and a strong base produces a salt and water.

$$HCl + NaOH \rightarrow NaCl + H_2O$$

	If the mixture is in stoichiometric proportions, the products will include 1 mole of water. This is responsible for the 18 mL excess volume.
Materials	Hydrochloric acid, 2 M, HCl (500 mL) Sodium hydroxide, 2 M, NaOH (500 mL) 500-mL Volumetric flask (2) 1-L Volumetric flask 25-mL Graduated cylinder
Safety Precautions	Sodium hydroxide is caustic, corrosive to body tissue and is very dangerous to eyes. Hydrochloric acid is severely corrosive to skin and eyes and highly toxic by ingestion or inhalation. Wear chemical splash goggles, chemical-resistant gloves and a chemical-resistant apron.
Preparation	Prepare (see page A) or purchase HCl and NaOH solutions. If preparing solutions, carefully follow directions in the *Flinn Chemical Catalog/Reference Manual:* always add acid to water and cool the NaOH solution during preparation.
	Measure out solutions and store in 500-mL volumetric flasks until demonstration.
Demonstration	Pour the sodium hydroxide solution into the 1-liter volumetric flask. Add the hydrochloric acid solution slowly, swirling as you do so to ensure mixing. When all the acid has been added, it will be seen that the volume of solution in the flask is greater than 1 liter. Remove this excess with a dropper pipette and transfer it to a 25-mL graduated cylinder. The volume should be very close to 18 mL.
Disposal	The solution can be flushed down the drain with excess water.

Acid–Water Puzzle

Demonstrate the behavior of an acid as it is diluted.

Application | Solutions • Heat of Solution • Exothermic Reactions • Colligative Properties

Theory | When sulfuric acid is added to water, the solution process is highly exothermic and the temperature of the system rises rapidly. If the acid is added to an equal mass of ice instead, the temperature is depressed well below the normal freezing point of water, due to the nature of the solution. This is an example of a colligative property. This is why salt is added to the ice in an ice cream freezer. The ice can continue to absorb heat from the mixture until its freezing point is reached. After this temperature is reached, the heat absorbed by the melting ice maintains the temperature.

Materials | Sulfuric acid, 9 M, H_2SO_4 (200 mL)
250-mL Beakers (2)
Ice
Thermometers (2)
Distilled or deionized water
100-mL Graduated cylinders (2)

Safety Precautions | Sulfuric acid is severely corrosive to eyes, skin and other tissue; considerable heat of dilution with water; even very dilute solutions are harmful to eyes and skin. Wear chemical splash goggles, chemical-resistant gloves and a chemical-resistant apron.

Preparation | Prepare or purchase the 9 M H_2SO_4 solution: To prepare, slowly add 100 mL of concentrated H_2SO_4 to about 100 g of ice, dilute to a total of 200 mL. This should be done in advance, so that the solution is at room temperature for the demo. Use ice to cool some water down to 0 °C.

Demonstration | Place 100 mL of ice water in a 250-mL beaker. Have a student measure its temperature. Measure the temperature of the acid solution. Ask students to predict what the result of mixing the solutions will be. Slowly add 100 mL of the 9 M acid to the water. Always add acid to water, never the reverse. Stir, and record the temperature. There should be a rise of about 18 to 20 °C.

Place 100 grams of ice into the other beaker. Have a student measure the temperature. Ask students to predict what will happen when the acid is added. Slowly add 100 mL of the 9 M acid. Stir, and measure the temperature. Most students are surprised to see that a temperature of about –15 °C is obtained.

Disposal | The sulfuric acid should be neutralized according to Flinn Suggested Disposal Method #24b before flushing down the drain with excess water.

Reference | Summerlin, L., et al. *Chemical Demonstrations;* American Chemical Society: Washington, DC, 1988; Vol. 2, p 101.

Salting Out — Making Liquids Immiscible

Show how competition for solvent molecules can affect miscibility.

Application	Solutions • Solvation • Solubility
Theory	Methanol and water are miscible in all proportions and form a homogeneous solution. If potassium carbonate is added to such a solution, it dissolves. Since potassium carbonate is an ionic solid, it dissociates. The equation is:

$$K_2CO_3(s) \rightarrow 2K^+(aq) + CO_3^{2-}(aq)$$

The resulting ions compete with methanol molecules for available solvent molecules. Since charges on the ions produce a greater attraction for water molecules than the dipole–dipole interaction between methanol and water, the dissociated ions are winners in the competition. Thus, as the amount of dissolved potassium carbonate increases, methanol will be forced out of solution. The mixture will separate into two distinct layers.

Materials	Distilled or deionized water (150 mL) Methanol, ethanol may be substituted (150 mL) Potassium carbonate, K_2CO_3 (100 g) 600-mL Beaker Magnetic stirrer
Safety Precautions	Methanol is flammable, a dangerous fire risk and toxic by ingestion. Potassium carbonate solution can irritate skin and eyes. Wear chemical splash goggles, chemical-resistant gloves and a chemical-resistant apron.
Preparation	Divide the potassium carbonate into four 25-g samples.
Demonstration	Mix 150 mL of distilled water and 150 mL of methanol in a 600-mL beaker. Place the beaker on the magnetic stirrer and begin stirring. Add 25 g of potassium carbonate and allow it to dissolve completely. Add the other 25 g samples in the same manner, allowing each to dissolve before adding the next. Distinct liquid layers will become visible.
Disposal	The solution can be flushed down the drain with excess water.
Reference	Shakashiri, B. Z. *Chemical Demonstrations;* University of Wisconsin: Madison, WI 1989; Vol. 3, p 266.

Supersaturated Solution

Show that a supersaturated solution is very unstable and can be changed to a saturated solution in a number of ways.

Application   Solubility • Supersaturation • Solutions

Theory   A supersaturated solution is one which is holding more solute in solution than can normally be dissolved at that temperature. The solution requires a stimulus to start the crystallization process. This can be a very small crystal (seed crystal) of the solute or simply a violent shake. Sodium acetate is used because of the large difference in solubility with temperature.

Materials   Sodium acetate, $CH_3CO_2Na \cdot 3H_2O$ (50 g)
250-mL Florence flask
50-mL Buret

Safety Precautions   Sodium acetate is a skin, eye and respiratory irritant. Be careful in handling the hot solution and do not heat the solution with the stopper in place. Wear chemical splash goggles, chemical-resistant gloves and a chemical-resistant apron.

Preparation   Prepare the solution: Place approximately 50 grams of sodium acetate in a very clean 250-mL Florence flask. Add 5 mL of water and slowly warm until the solid completely dissolves. Wash down the neck and sides of the flask to dissolve any solid. Remove the flask from heat and allow it to cool to room temperature or below.

Demonstration   **Crystallization procedure 1:**
Add a very small seed crystal to the solution and watch it became almost completely solid in a matter of 2 or 3 seconds. The solution can be reused an unlimited number of times.

Crystallization procedure 2:
The solution must be very cold. Immerse in ice water bath for fifteen minutes. Remove it from the ice water and give it a violent shake. It will immediately become solid. Again the solution may be heated and reused.

Crystallization procedure 3:
Pour the solution while still warm into a 50-mL buret. Cool to room temperature or below. Place a few crystals of the solute on a clean lab table or Petri dish and set up the buret above the crystals. Slowly drip the solution from the buret onto the crystals and a tall column of crystals will be formed.

Disposal   Sodium acetate should be reused, no disposal is required.

A Coin-Operated Reaction

Three interconnected flasks each containing colorless liquids yield red, white and blue solutions when a coin is added to the first flask.

Application | Acids and Bases • Pressure

Theory | Three flasks, A, B and C, each contain three different liquids. Flask A contains a few milliliters of concentrated nitric acid, Flask B is filled with a dilute solution of nitric acid and phenolphthalein indicator, and Flask C is half-filled with a dilute solution of sodium hydroxide. Flasks A and B are sealed and connected to each other with glass tubing. Flask B is also connected to Flask C, which is not sealed.

Upon the addition of two pennies, the copper reacts with the concentrated nitric acid to form the red-brown nitrogen dioxide gas and a solution of cupric nitrate. As the gas continues to form it is forced into Flask B. Subsequently, as the pressure increases, the dilute nitric acid in Flask B is forced into Flask C. Since the dilute nitric acid contains phenolphthalein, the solution in Flask C turns a pink-red color. As the concentrated nitric acid in Flask A is consumed, the reaction begins to slow and Flask A begins to cool causing the nitrogen dioxide to contract and in turn creates a vacuuming effect on the contents of Flask B. The highly soluble nitrogen dioxide gas contributes to this vacuuming effect by dissolving in the dilute nitric acid solution of Flask B which in turn creates a vacuum force on the contents of Flask C. As the dilute nitric acid solution from Flask B enters Flask A, it dilutes the blue-colored solution of cupric nitrate and eventually fills half of Flask A. The red-colored basic solution from Flask C enters the acidic Flask B, changes to a colorless solution, leaving Flask B half filled. Flask C is left half filled with a red-colored solution. Red, white and blue—patriotic colors.

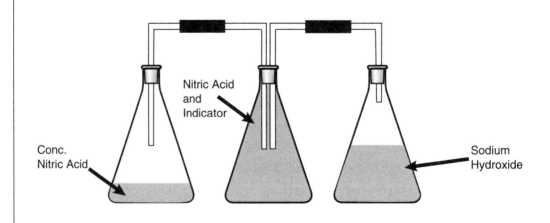

Conc. Nitric Acid

Nitric Acid and Indicator

Sodium Hydroxide

Materials	500-mL Erlenmeyer flasks (3)
	1-hole Stopper
	2-hole Stopper (2)
	Glass tubing, "L"-shaped (4)
	Nitric acid, conc. 16 M, HNO_3, (15 mL)
	Nitric acid, 0.10 M, HNO_3 (600 mL)
	Sodium hydroxide, 0.35 M, NaOH (200 mL)
	Shiny copper pennies (3)
	Flexible cold pack (optional)
	Phenolphthalein

Safety Precautions

Nitric acid is corrosive; strong oxidant; toxic by inhalation; avoid contact with acetic acid and readily oxidized substances. Use pennies dated prior to 1982. Beginning in 1982, the U.S. mint began minting pennies from copper-electroplated zinc. Beware, as zinc reacts violently with nitric acid. Nitrogen dioxide is highly toxic, keep contained in apparatus until it fully dissolves in the aqueous solution. Sodium hydroxide is corrosive and very dangerous to eyes. Wear chemical splash goggles, chemical-resistant gloves and a chemical-resistant apron.

Preparation

Prepare 4 "L"-shaped pieces of glass tubing. Three of these pieces should extend halfway into the Erlenmeyer flasks, to the 250-mL mark, when attached through a rubber stopper. The fourth piece of glass should extend only about an inch into the flask. Connect the tubing with latex or rubber tubing and set up the apparatus as shown in the diagram.

Pour 15 mL concentrated nitric acid into Flask A and secure the 1-hole stopper. Place 1 mL phenolphthalein into Flask B and fill completely with the dilute nitric acid solution (about 600 mL) and secure the 2-hole rubber stopper. Pour 200 mL of the sodium hydroxide solution into Flask C.

Demonstration

Remove the stopper from Flask A and drop 2 to 3 copper pennies into Flask A. Quickly secure the stopper. Let the reaction proceed while holding a discussion as to the reactions taking place. The reactions may take as long as 10 minutes. In order to increase the flow of the solutions from flask to flask, a flexible cold pack can be placed under Flask A to cool it more quickly.

Disposal

The copper pennies should be rinsed and reused. All solutions can be flushed down the drain with excess water.

Reference

Perkins, R. I. *J. Chem. Ed,* **1986,** *63,* 783.

Solubility Product Constant, K_{sp}

Formation of a precipitate and its gradual disappearance emphasizes the solubility product equilibrium constant.

Application

Solubility • K_{sp} • Precipitation

Theory

Slightly soluble substances can be treated as equilibrium systems. If "XY" is such a substance, then a mixture of XY and water can be written as

$$XY(s) \rightarrow X^+(aq) + Y^-(aq)$$

The solubility product equilibrium constant, K_{sp}, would be defined as $[X^+][Y^-]$, where brackets indicate the molar concentration. If solutions containing X^+ and Y^- are mixed, and the resulting concentrations are such that $[X^+][Y^-]$ is larger than K_{sp}, XY(s) will form. However, if $[X^+][Y^-]$ is less than K_{sp}, there is no precipitate.

The precipitation of lead iodide from lead nitrate and potassium iodide and then the gradual disappearance of the precipitate emphasize the concept of dilution (concentration) on the maintenance of the precipitate. The K_{sp} of lead iodide is 8.5×10^{-9}.

Materials

1000-mL Graduated cylinder
Potassium iodide, 0.1 M, KI (100 mL)
Lead nitrate, 0.01 M, $Pb(NO_3)_2$ (1 L)

Safety Precautions

Lead nitrate is toxic by inhalation and ingestion, and a strong oxidant. Wear chemical splash goggles and always follow laboratory safety rules while performing demonstrations.

Preparation

Dissolve 1.66 g of KI in enough water to produce 100 mL of solution.
Dissolve 3.31 g of $Pb(NO_3)_2$ in enough water to produce one liter of solution.

Demonstration

A 1000-mL cylinder is filled with 0.01 M lead nitrate solution and placed on a light box. Use the overhead stage if no light box is available. To the contents of the cylinder, add one drop of 0.1 M potassium iodide solution.

When the precipitate disappears, add another drop of the KI. Many drops may be added before exhausting the lead ions. Save the solutions for use year after year.

Use of the light box emphasizes the precipitate and makes it more visible. Try this one in a buret so accurate measurements may be made as to when the precipitate actually disappears. If one drop is 0.05 mL and it enters the top 1 mL of the buret, the concentrations can be readily calculated. K_{sp} values can be derived from these data. Successive calculations will show you where the precipitate will be predicted to disappear. Then test your prediction.

Disposal

Dispose of lead solution by Flinn Suggested Disposal Method #27f.

Conductivity Puzzle

Demonstrate that the reaction of two weak electrolytes produces a good conductor of electricity.

Application | Acids and Bases • Electrolyte • Neutralization

Theory | Weak acids and weak bases are poor conductors of electricity due to their incomplete ionization. When they are mixed together, they neutralize each other. The products are water and a salt. The reaction is as follows:

$$HC_2H_3O_2(aq) + NH_4OH(aq) \rightarrow H_2O(l) + NH_4C_2H_3O_2(aq)$$

The salt is dissociated completely into NH_4^+ ions and $C_2H_3O_2^-$ ions, so the resulting solution is a strong electrolyte.

Materials | Acetic acid, 1 M, $HC_2H_3O_2$ (250 mL)
Ammonium hydroxide, 1 M, NH_4OH (250 mL)
250-mL Beakers (3)
Conductivity apparatus
Distilled or deionized water for rinsing electrodes
Stirring rod

Safety Precautions | Ammonia solutions are extremely irritating to skin and eyes and the vapor is a respiratory irritant. Ammonia is toxic by ingestion and inhalation. Acetic acid solutions are corrosive, toxic by ingestion and a mild fire risk. Wear chemical splash goggles, chemical-resistant gloves and a chemical-resistant apron.

Preparation | Prepare (see page A) or purchase solutions.

Demonstration | Turn the conductivity apparatus on. Test the acetic acid solution, the bulb will glow faintly. Rinse the electrodes with distilled water. Test the ammonia solution. The bulb will be even fainter. Rinse the electrodes. Now pour about half of the acetic acid solution into a clean dry 250-mL beaker, then add about the same volume of the ammonia solution. Stir, and test the conductivity of the mixture. The bulb now glows very brightly.

Disposal | Solution can be flushed down the drain with excess water.

Reference | Shakashiri, B. Z. *Chemical Demonstrations;* University of Wisconsin: Madison, WI, Vol. 3, p 326.

Ammonia Fountain

The extreme solubility of ammonia in water is used to produce a partial vacuum.

Application | Solubility • Neutralization • Indicator • Gas Pressure • Acids and Bases

Theory | Ammonia is extremely soluble in water. A partial vacuum can be formed in a flask filled with ammonia if a few drops of water are squirted into the flask. Air pressure will push water up into the flask. If phenolphthalein is added to the water in the beaker, a pink color will show the presence of a base.

Materials | Ammonia
(cylinder of dry gas is best but generating from concentrated reagent is possible)
Round bottom flask with 2-hole stopper
400-mL Beaker
Glass tubing, 40 cm
Ring stand with ring
Medicine dropper

Safety Precautions | Ammonia is severely toxic and irritating by inhalation and may be fatal. Use only under a fume hood. Ammonia is also a moderate fire risk. Wear chemical splash goggles, chemical-resistant gloves and a chemical-resistant apron.

Preparation | Ammonia gas may be generated by gently heating concentrated ammonia solution (12 M) on a hot plate using a one-hole stopper/delivery tube setup.

Prepare the apparatus as shown:

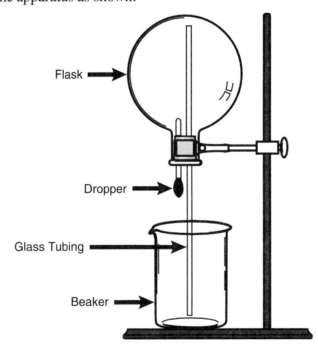

Flask

Dropper

Glass Tubing

Beaker

Demonstration | Fill a round bottom flask with dry ammonia gas (from a lecture bottle). Affix a 2-hole stopper containing a medicine dropper and a 40-cm glass tube to the flask. Invert the flask and place the glass tube into a beaker filled with water and phenolphthalein. Squirt a few drops of water from the dropper into the flask containing ammonia gas. Ammonia will dissolve into the few droplets of water resulting in a vacuum being produced. The vacuum will cause the water from the beaker to be drawn up into the flask. As the water enters the flask with the ammonia, the phenolphthalein will turn pink due to the alkaline ammonia solution.

Disposal | All solutions may be flushed down a sink with excess water.

Multi-Colored Ammonia Fountain

The extreme solubility of ammonia in water is used to produce a partial vacuum.

Application | Solubility • Neutralization • Universal Indicator • Gas Pressure

Theory | A solution spontaneously enters a tiered four-flask system filled with ammonia gas. This results in a rainbow of colors. By opening the top valve, the solution drains back into the original container reversing the color changes.

Materials | Ammonia
  (cylinder of dry gas is best but generating from concentrated reagent is possible)
Universal indicator, 10 mL
Acetic acid, 6 M, $HC_2H_3O_2$
Round bottom flasks with 2-hole stoppers (3)
Separatory funnel with one-hole stopper (1)
Large beaker
U-shaped pieces of glass tubing, see diagram (3)
Long, straight tube (1)
Ring stand
Utility clamps (4)

Safety Precautions | Ammonia is severely toxic and irritating by inhalation and may be fatal. Use only under a fume hood. Ammonia is also a moderate fire risk. Acetic acid is corrosive to skin and tissue, toxic by ingestion and a moderate fire risk. Wear chemical splash goggles, chemical-resistant gloves and a chemical-resistant apron.

Preparation | Ammonia gas may be generated by gently heating concentrated ammonia solution (12 M) on a hot plate using a one-hole stopper/delivery tube setup.

Prepare the apparatus as shown:

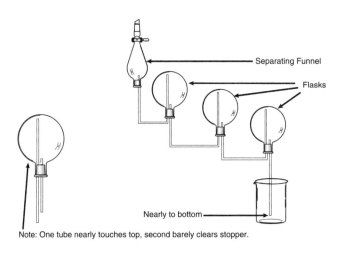

Separating Funnel

Flasks

Nearly to bottom

Note: One tube nearly touches top, second barely clears stopper.

Demonstration	Charge the apparatus in the fume hood or outdoors with ammonia from the top down. Be certain that the valve of the separatory funnel is open, flush thoroughly with 3 to 5 minutes of moderate flow, then close the valve.
	Fill the beaker with the acetic acid solution, 6.8 mL of 6 M acid per liter of water. Add the indicator solution and stir. Set the open tube into the beaker as shown. Fill the tube of the separatory funnel with water from a wash bottle.
	Quickly open the valve to admit a few drops of water and quickly close it again before all the water enters. Watch as the water is drawn into the apparatus. Note the color changes and pH values observed. When complete, open the valve and allow air pressure to push the water back into the beaker.
Disposal	All solutions may be flushed down a sink with excess water.
Reference	Bob Becker, Kirkwood High School, Kirkwood, MO.

Chemiluminescent Ammonia Fountain

The vacuum produced in an ammonia fountain is used to mix the solutions of a chemiluminescent demo.

Application | Chemiluminescence • Solubility • Neutralization • Pressure

Theory | Ammonia is extremely soluble in water. A partial vacuum can be formed in a flask filled with ammonia if a few drops of water are squirted into the flask. Air pressure will push water up into the flask. If phenolphthalein is added to the water in the beaker, a pink color will show the presence of a base.

Exothermic reactions yield energy. Chemiluminescent reactions yield light energy. Fireflies produce their flashes of light through chemiluminescent reactions.

Materials | Ring stand with clamp
2-L Round bottom flask
2-hole Rubber stopper
Medicine dropper or pipet
Glass tubing (40 cm)
1-L Erlenmeyer flasks (2)
Rubber tubing, 1-inch
Glass Tubing, L-shaped pieces (2)
Ammonia gas, NH_3
Sodium carbonate, Na_2CO_3
Luminol, 3-aminophthalhydrazide, available from Flinn: L0031
Distilled water
Sodium bicarbonate, $NaHCO_3$
Ammonium carbonate, $(NH_4)CO_3$
Cupric sulfate, $CuSO_4 \cdot 5H_2O$
Hydrogen peroxide, 3% solution, H_2O_2

Safety Precautions | Ammonia is severely toxic and irritating by inhalation and may be fatal. Use only under a fume hood. Ammonia is also a moderate fire risk. Sodium carbonate may be a skin irritant. Wear chemical splash goggles, chemical-resistant gloves and a chemical-resistant apron.

Preparation	Prepare the solutions as follows:

Solution A:
In a 1000-mL flask, dissolve 4.0 g of sodium carbonate in approximately 600 mL of distilled water. Add 0.2 g of luminol, stir to dissolve. Add 24.0 g of sodium bicarbonate, 0.5 g of ammonium carbonate monohydrate and 0.4 g of cupric sulfate. Stir to dissolve solution. Dilute to 1000 mL.

Solution B:
In a 1000-mL flask, add 50 mL of 3% hydrogen peroxide, dilute to 1000 mL and mix well. Prepare this solution within an hour of performing the demonstration.

Demonstration

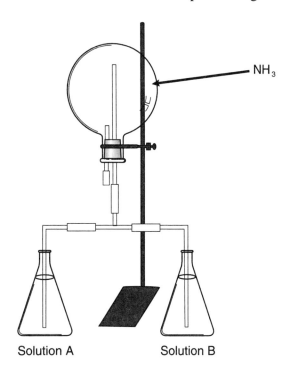

NH$_3$

Solution A   Solution B

Fill a round bottom flask with dry ammonia gas (from a lecture bottle) and set up the apparatus as in the diagram. Squirt a few drops of water from the dropper into the flask. Ammonia will dissolve into the few droplets of water resulting in a vacuum being produced. The vacuum will cause the two solutions to be drawn up into the flask. In turn the solutions will mix producing a second reaction which results in chemiluminescent effects.

Disposal   Solution may be flushed down the drain with excess water.

Reference   Thomas, N. *J. Chem. Ed.* **1990,** *67,* 359.

Colloids Exhibiting the Tyndall Effect

The properties of colloids are investigated and compared to those of solutions.

Application | Colloids • Tyndall Effect • Suspensions • Solutions • Emulsions

Theory | A colloid is a mixture in which the size of the mixed particles are between those of a solution and a suspension. Solutions are homogeneous mixtures in which the size of the dissolved particles are one-millionth of a millimeter in diameter. A suspension is a heterogeneous mixture in which the particles are large enough to be seen with a microscope or unaided eye. Colloidal particles appear evenly distributed when viewed with a microscope.

Examples of colloids include foams such as whipped cream (gas in liquid) and marshmallows (gas in solid), aerosols such as fog and clouds (liquid in gas), emulsions such as milk, mayonnaise and salad dressings (liquid in liquid) or cheese and butter (liquid in solid), smoke such as dust and smog (solid in gas), and sols such as jellies, and latex paint (solid in liquid) or pearls and opals (solid in solid).

Colloids exhibit two interesting properties. If a beam of light is passed through a colloid, the colloid will scatter the light. That is, the beam will become visible in the colloid. This phenomenon is called the Tyndall Effect. Colloids also exhibit Brownian Motion. If a colloid is looked at under a microscope its colloidal particles will appear to move in a random zig-zag motion called Brownian Motion. The larger, visible particles move in such a manner because they are colliding continuously with smaller, invisible particles in the mixture.

Materials | Milk (5 mL)
Aquarium, or large beaker (2)
Glass stirring rod
Salt (50 g)
Prepared gelatin, in a square glass container
Shaving cream or whipped cream
Aerosol spray
Laser or mini-mag flashlight with focusing beam
Samples of solutions (e.g., soda pop, salt water, food coloring)

Safety Precautions | Do not point the laser at anyone. Even a short flash of laser light into an eye can cause permanent damage. Wear chemical splash goggles and always follow laboratory safety rules while performing demonstrations.

Preparation | Fill two aquariums with water. One aquarium will serve as a control.

Demonstration	To one aquarium, add a few milliliters of milk to form a colloidal mixture. Only add enough milk so the mixture is colloidal but not yet opaque. Darken the room and allow a laser beam to pass through the colloidal mixture.
	Allow the laser beam to pass through the control. Add about 50 g salt to the control. Allow the laser beam to pass through the saltwater solution. Discuss the properties of colloids in contrast to solutions.
	Test other substances and determine if they are colloids or not.
Disposal	Solution can be flushed down the drain with excess water.

Burning Gel

Combining two liquids forms a gel that is combustible.

Application | Organic Chemistry • Combustion • Exothermic Reactions • Colloids

Theory | Isopropyl alcohol dehydrates a saturated solution of calcium acetate forming an alcohol rich gel caused by competition for solvent molecules. The solubility of calcium acetate is decreased, forming a lattice of solids which traps alcohol molecules inside. The gel burns quietly with a blue flame leaving a white calcium oxide/carbonate residue.

$$Ca(C_2H_3O_2)_2 + (CH_3)_2CHOH + O_2 \rightarrow CO_2 + H_2O + CaO + CaCO_3$$

Note; this is not a polymerization reaction, it results in the formation of a colloidal suspension.

Materials | Calcium acetate, saturated solution, $Ca(C_2H_3O_2)_2$ (20 mL)
2-Propanol, iso-propyl alcohol, C_3H_7OH (100 mL)
200-mL Beaker
Stirring rod
Non-combustible surface
Ethanol, optional—may be substituted for propanol

Safety Precautions | 2-Propanol and ethanol are flammable liquids and dangerous fire risks. 2-Propanol is harmful to eyes and respiratory tract. Cover work surface with non-flammable material when burning gel. Wash hands after handling gel and before igniting it. Wear chemical splash goggles, chemical-resistant gloves and a chemical-resistant apron.

Preparation | Prepare a saturated solution of calcium acetate (35 g/100 mL) by putting distilled water into a beaker full of calcium acetate crystals and allowing to stand overnight. If not saturated add more crystals or use a magnetic stirrer.

Demonstration | Put 20 mL of the acetate solution into the beaker. Quickly add 100 mL of the alcohol to form the gel. When gel is completely formed, remove with your hand (wear gloves) and squeeze excess alcohol from it. Place the solid mass on the non-flammable surface. Wash gloves/hands with copious amounts of water.

Ignite the mass with a match or lighter. Try adding a few drops of a salt solution ($CuCl_2$) to attain a colored flame.

Disposal | Burn all of the gel in the fume hood. The white residue may be flushed down the drain. Evaporate excess alcohol to dryness in the hood according to Flinn Suggested Disposal Method #18a.

Reference | Shakashiri, B. Z. *Chemical Demonstrations;* University of Wisconsin: Madison, WI, 1989; Vol. 3, p 360.

Chemical Sunset

Demonstrate the formation of colloidal suspensions.

Application	Colloids • Tyndall Effect • Redox • Solutions
Theory	The major difference between a solution and a colloid is the size of the particles in the mixture. In a solution, the particles are molecular in nature and size, while in a colloid, they are larger, but still small enough to remain suspended in the solvent. The production of colloidal sulfur is a two-step reaction.

$$2H^+(aq) + S_2O_3^{2-}(aq) \rightarrow H_2S_2O_3(aq)$$

$$H_2S_2O_3(aq) \rightarrow H_2SO_3(aq) + S(s)$$

Produce a slight scattering of blue light through the solution. Initially, the sulfur particles are very small and thus can only scatter the shortest wavelengths of visible light (blue and violet). As the amount of sulfur increases, more and more of these short wavelengths are scattered, and the transmitted light takes on a reddish-brown hue.

Materials	Overhead projector / Sodium thiosulfate, 10% solution, $Na_2S_2O_3$ Hydrochloric acid, 1 M, HCl (10 mL) / 600-mL Beaker or crystallizing dish Sharp knife or single-edge razor blade / Stirring rod Posterboard
Safety Precautions	Hydrochloric acid is severely corrosive to skin and eyes and highly toxic by ingestion or inhalation. Wear chemical splash goggles, chemical-resistant gloves and a chemical-resistant apron.
Preparation	Prepare 10% Sodium thiosulfate solution by dissolving approximately 70 grams in 400 mL of distilled or deionized water. Cut a piece of posterboard that is slightly larger than the overhead projector stage. Cut a round hole in the center of the posterboard that is a little smaller than the diameter of the beaker.
Demonstration	Fill the beaker with the sodium thiosulfate solution. Place the posterboard on the overhead stage and put the beaker over the hole. Focus the projector to get a bright spot on the screen. Note that the solution is clear when viewed from the side. Add 2 to 3 drops of the HCl solution and stir. Note how the mixture becomes slightly cloudy and takes on a bluish cast. Note any changes in the color of the projected spot. Add a few more drops of HCl and stir. Repeat observations. Continue to add HCl and soon the projected spot will become too dark to see.
Disposal	Solution can be flushed down the drain with excess water.
References	Shakhashiri, B. Z. *Chemical Demonstrations;* University of Wisconsin: Madison, WI, 1989; Vol. 3, p 353. Goldsmith, R. H. *J. Chem. Educ.* **1988**, *65,* 623.

Ammonia Bottle

A crushing variation on the ammonia fountain demonstration.

Application | Gases • Solubility • Pressure

Theory | Ammonia gas has a very high solubility in water. This has often been used to produce the classic ammonia fountain demo in a round bottom flask (see pg. 148). As the ammonia gas dissolves in a small amount of water, the pressure inside the container drops, creating a vacuum. This demonstration uses a plastic 2-liter soda bottle which is crushed by atmospheric pressure as the internal pressure is reduced by the ammonia solubility.

Materials |
2-L Soda bottle
1-hole Rubber stopper
Glass tubing, short piece

Ammonium hydroxide, conc., NH_4OH (15–20 mL)
Plastic syringe, 10–20 mL size
Rubber tubing, short piece

Safety Precautions | Ammonium hydroxide liquid and vapor are extremely irritating—especially to eyes. Also toxic by inhalation and ingestion. Serious respiratory hazard, dispense in a hood. Wear chemical splash goggles, chemical-resistant gloves and a chemical-resistant apron.

Preparation | Make up the stopper assembly by inserting a short piece of glass tubing into the rubber stopper. Fill the syringe with water and connect it to the glass tubing using a short length of rubber or plastic tubing. In a fume hood, pour 15 to 20 mL of the concentrated aqueous ammonia into the soda bottle, cap tightly, and agitate for a few seconds. Remove the cap carefully—gas pressure can cause some of the ammonia solution to spray out. Insert the stopper assembly. Do this immediately before the demonstration.

Demonstration | Explain to the students that the bottle is full of ammonia gas. Ask them to predict what will happen when water is added to this bottle from the syringe. Some may expect the bottle to bulge. Press the syringe. The bottle will immediately collapse as the ammonia gas dissolves in the added water. The degree of collapse depends on several factors, including the amount of water added and the concentration of ammonia.

Disposal | Rinse bottle out with water before disposing in the trash.

Reference | Sheets, Michael. *J. Chem. Ed.* **1991,** *68,* 247.

Chapter 13

Acids/Bases

Classical Properties of Acids and Bases

Demonstrate the classical behavior of acids and bases.

Application | Acids and Bases • Physical Properties

Theory | Acids are a group of substances which have a sour taste, change the color of some plant pigments, and dissolve certain minerals and metals. Bases are substances which have a soapy feeling, reverse the color changes of plant pigments altered by acids, and when combined with acids in the proper proportions, destroy the properties of the acids. The classification of some substances as acids and others as bases is one of the oldest in chemistry, and the terms acid, alkali and salt can be found in writings of medieval alchemists. Acids were probably the more easily recognized of the two substances because of their sour taste. Other properties associated with acids include the ability to dissolve many metals, and produce bubbles when combined with some minerals, such as carbonates. On the other hand, the most notable property of bases is their ability to neutralize acids.

Materials | Distilled water
Hydrochloric acid, 2 M, HCl (450 mL)
Sulfuric acid, 2 M, H_2SO_4 (450 mL)
Acetic acid, 2 M, $HC_2H_3O_2$ (450 mL)
Blue litmus paper (8 strips)
Magnesium metal ribbon or turnings, Mg
Cupric carbonate, $CuCO_3$ (40 g)
Sodium hydroxide, 6 M, NaOH (600 mL)
Stirring rods (12)
250-mL Beakers (12)
Labels for beakers (12)

Safety Precautions | Sulfuric acid, hydrochloric acid, and acetic acid are severely corrosive to eyes, skin, and other tissue and toxic by ingestion and inhalation. When making solutions, always add acid to water, never the reverse; considerable heat of dilution will occur. Sodium hydroxide is a corrosive solid and skin burns are possible. Significant heat evolves when added to water and solutions are very dangerous to eyes and skin. Cupric carbonate is toxic by ingestion. Magnesium metal is a flammable solid. Wear chemical splash goggles, chemical-resistant gloves and a chemical-resistant apron.

Preparation | Prepare (see page A) or purchase all solutions described above. Arrange the 12 beakers in three sets of four. Label one beaker in each set H_2O, another HCl, another H_2SO_4, and the last $HC_2H_3O_2$.

Demonstration Fill each beaker about half way with the appropriate material. Place a stirring rod in each beaker. Dip a strip of blue litmus paper into each beaker of each set. The strip dipped in the water will become a deeper blue but the ones dipped in the acids will become pink. Save the strips. Drop some magnesium metal into each beaker of the same set. The magnesium dissolves, emitting gas bubbles as it does so.

Place 5 g of cupric carbonate into each of the four beakers in another set. Stir the mixture and note what happens in each beaker.

Put about 150 mL of the 6 M NaOH into each of the four beakers of the last set and stir. Test the liquids in these beakers with fresh strips of blue litmus paper, and with the strips used earlier to test the first set of beakers. Note the changes. Now place 5 g of cupric carbonate into each of the beakers in the last set, stir the mixtures and note how these results differ from those obtained with the second set of beakers.

Disposal Neutralize the bases and acids according to Flinn Suggested Disposal Methods #10 and #24b respectively.

Reference Shakashiri, B. Z. *Chemical Demonstrations;* University of Wisconsin: Madison, WI, 1988; Vol. 3, p 60.

Overhead Acid/Base Indicators

Show the characteristic behavior of an indicator solution using the overhead projector.

Application	Acids and Bases • pH • Indicators
Theory	Indicators are substances which give a visible sign, usually a color change, of the presence or absence of another substance. Indicators which respond to the concentration of hydrogen ion or hydroxide ion in solution are known as pH indicators. Each indicator has a characteristic pH range through which it undergoes its color change. Some are limited to two colors, e.g., methyl red. Others such as bromothymol blue have many different colors.
Materials	Overhead projector Distilled or de-ionized water Hydrogen chloride, 6 M, HCl (71 mL) Sodium hydroxide, 6 M, NaOH (70 mL) Ammonium chloride, 1 M, NH_4Cl (60 mL) Clear acetate sheet Transparency marker 100-mL Beakers (6) Stirring rods (6) Bromothymol blue indicator
Safety Precautions	Hydrochloric acid is highly toxic by ingestion or inhalation and severely corrosive to skin and eyes. Solid sodium hydroxide is caustic, corrosive to body tissue. Solutions are very dangerous to the eyes. Both substances evolve considerable heat when added to water. Ammonium chloride is toxic by ingestion. Wear chemical splash goggles, chemical-resistant gloves and a chemical-resistant apron.
Preparation	Prepare the solutions listed above or purchase from Flinn Scientific. Label and fill the beakers as follows:

Label	Prep
A) 6 M HCl	60 mL of 6 M HCl.
B) 1 M HCl	10 mL of 6 M HCl and 50 mL of distilled water.
C) 0.1 M HCl	1 mL of 6 M HCl and 60 mL of distilled water.
D) 1 M NH_4Cl	60 mL of 1 M NH_4Cl.
E) 1 M NaOH	10 mL of 6 M NaOH and 50 mL of distilled water.
F) 6 M NaOH	60 mL of 6 M NaOH.

Demonstration	Write six labels on the transparency using the marker, and place each beaker next to its appropriate label. Put 10 drops of the bromothymol blue indicator into each beaker and stir. Each beaker will be a different color.
Disposal	Carefully combine the waste solutions to neutralize them and then flush down the drain with plenty of water.
References	Shakhashiri, B. Z. *Chemical Demonstrations;* University of Wisconsin: Madison, WI, 1989; Vol. 3, p 38.
	Kolb, D. *J. Chem. Educ.* **1987,** *64,* 348.

Red Cabbage — A Great Indicator

An easy method of extracting acid/base indicators from plants.

Application | Acids and Bases • Indicators • Household Chemistry

Theory | Many plant extracts have been found to act as excellent acid/base indicators. Red cabbage juice is probably the more widely prepared extract among high school science teachers. Most teachers find themselves dreading the traditional technique of boiling red cabbage leaves in order to extract the cabbage juice. If all that is needed is the juice—why not puree the leaves in a blender and pour off the juice. This process takes only a few seconds and does not stink up the science hallway. The method may also be used to extract indicators from other plants such as beets, onions, radishes, spinach, rose petals, brussel sprouts, among others.

Materials |
Red cabbage leaves (2 to 3)　　　Distilled water
Blender　　　Vinegar
Buret (2)　　　Ring stand with buret clamp
600-mL Beaker (2)　　　Household ammonia
Magnetic stir bar　　　Magnetic stirrer

Safety Precautions | Never eat food in a chemistry lab. Once a food product is brought into a lab it is considered contaminated and not safe for consumption. Wear chemical splash goggles and always follow laboratory safety rules while performing demonstrations.

Preparation | None required.

Demonstration | Take a few leaves and place in a blender with about 300 mL distilled water. Blend until the leaves are fully pureed. Decant or filter the liquid. This liquid may now be used as an excellent indicator for acids and bases.

Set up a buret clamped to a ring stand. Fill one buret with vinegar and the other with ammonia. Fill a 600-mL beaker filled with 200 mL ammonia and 20 mL of the red cabbage indicator. Prepare an identical beaker as a control and set aside. Place a magnetic stir bar in the beaker. Set the beaker on top of a magnetic stirrer under the tip of the buret filled with vinegar. Allow the vinegar to slowly drip into the stirring ammonia solution. Compare the color changes to the control. The color change should range from yellow, green, blue, violet to red.

Position the ammonia-filled buret over the same beaker and proceed to back titrate the solution to show that the color change of indicators is a reversible process.

Disposal | Solutions can be flushed down the drain with excess water.

Reference | Institute for Chemical Education, University of Wisconsin, Madison, WI, Summer 1989.

Household Acids, Bases and Indicators

Household products are identified as acids or bases using red cabbage juice and grape juice as indicators.

Application	Acids and Bases • Indicators • Household Chemistry
Theory	Many plant extracts have been found to act as excellent acid/base indicators. Red cabbage juice is probably the more widely prepared extract among high school science teachers. Many household products are acids or bases.
Safety Precautions	Never eat food in a chemistry lab. Once a food product is brought into a lab it is considered contaminated and not safe for consumption. Wear chemical splash goggles and always follow laboratory safety rules while performing demonstrations.
Materials	Red cabbage juice or unsweetened grape juice Vinegar Ammonia Dishwashing detergent Baking soda Washing soda Lemon juice Orange juice Ginger ale Hand soap Plastic cups, clear or beakers
Preparation	Add 5 mL of each of the materials to 100 mL of distilled water and place into different plastic cups. Label each container with its contents. Place these cups in random order so that students will have a chance to organize their observations.
Demonstration	Add drops of indicator to each solution until there is a notable color. The color range should be from red for acids to dark green or blue for bases. The darker the blue or green solution, the more basic the solution.
	To demonstrate the neutralization process, add drops of one of the bases to one of the acids until a purple color is reached. Show that the indicator is purple in a neutral solution such as distilled water.
Disposal	All solutions may be disposed of by flushing down a sink with excess water.

Dr. Jekyll's Home Brew

Demonstrate the reaction of an acid anhydride on an indicator solution.

Application | Acids and Bases • Indicators

Theory | When carbon dioxide dissolves in water, a weakly acidic solution of carbonic acid is produced. The reaction is:

$$CO_2(g) + H_2O(l) \rightarrow H_2CO_3(aq) \rightleftarrows H^+(aq) + HCO_3^-(aq)$$

The pH of the solution decreases. The change in pH is shown by the color change in universal indicator.

Materials | Dry ice, $CO_2(s)$
Universal indicator
Sodium hydroxide, 0.1 M, NaOH
250-mL Graduated cylinder or hydrometer jar
Water

Safety Precautions | Solid sodium hydroxide is caustic, corrosive to body tissue and solutions are dangerous to eyes. Dry ice should be handled with either forceps or gloves to prevent frostbite. Wear chemical splash goggles and always follow laboratory safety rules while performing demonstrations.

Demonstration | Fill the graduated cylinder with warm water to within about 5 cm of the top. Add about 10 mL of universal indicator, and a small amount of NaOH solution, just enough to get a definite blue-violet color. Place 4 or 5 pieces of dry ice into the cylinder. The bubbling begins immediately, and the indicator gradually changes color, showing increasing acidity. Students love the sight of the white water vapor pouring out of the top of the cylinder and falling to the desk top.

Disposal | The solution can be flushed down the drain with excess water.

Reference | Jeanette Hildenbrandt, State College Area High School North, State College, PA at Woodrow Wilson Chem 11 Institute.

The Rainbow Reaction

Demonstrate the pH range of Universal indicator.

Application | Acids and Bases • pH • Indicators • Diffusion of Liquids

Theory | Sodium carbonate solution is added to a solution of hydrochloric acid containing Universal indicator. The reaction is:

$$Na_2CO_3(aq) + 2\ HCl(aq) \rightarrow CO_2(g) + 2\ NaCl(aq) + H_2O(l)$$

As the reaction occurs, the concentration of the HCl solution is reduced. This has the effect of increasing the pH of the solution, causing the indicator to change color. The density of the sodium carbonate solution is sufficient to take it to the bottom of the container, so a color gradient can be seen.

Materials | Hydrochloric acid, 0.1 M , HCl (100 mL)
Sodium carbonate, saturated solution, Na_2CO_3 (100 mL)
Universal indicator
25 × 200 mm Test tube
Beral-type pipet, graduated
25-mL Graduated cylinder

Safety Precautions | Hydrochloric acid is highly toxic by ingestion or inhalation and severely corrosive to skin and eyes. Sodium carbonate may be a skin irritant. Universal indicator is an alcohol based, flammable liquid. Wear chemical splash goggles, chemical-resistant gloves and a chemical-resistant apron.

Preparation | Add 2.5 to 3 mL of Universal indicator to 100 mL of 0.1 M hydrochloric acid. Make up a saturated sodium carbonate solution by adding 13 g Na_2CO_3 to 100 mL of water.

Demonstration | Fill the 25 × 200 mm test tube almost full of the HCl – indicator solution. Fill the Beral pipet with the saturated sodium carbonate solution. Tilt the test tube slightly and squirt about one-third of the saturated Na_2CO_3 solution down the inside wall. Do not attempt to layer the solutions. The density of the Na_2CO_3 solution will cause it to settle to the bottom. Hold the test tube vertically and after a few seconds the colors will develop with the acidic red at the top and the basic deep blue at the bottom and a gradient in between. Practice! If the tube is then stoppered and clamped vertically, and left undisturbed, the color gradient will persist for as long as a couple of weeks, before becoming all one color. This demonstrates the very slow rate of diffusion in liquids.

Disposal | The dilute solutions can be flushed down the drain with excess water.

Reference | Summerlin, L., et al. *Chemical Demonstrations;* American Chemical Society: Washington, DC, 1988; Vol. 1, p 38.

The pH Concept

The color range of red cabbage indicator illustrates the concept of a pH scale.

Application | Acids and Bases • Indicators • pH • Titration

Theory | Many plant extracts have been found to act as excellent acid/base indicators. Red cabbage juice is probably the most widely prepared extract among high school science teachers. The color range for red cabbage indicator from basic to acidic is yellow, green, blue, violet to red, where blue is neutral. In order to quantify degree of acidity or basicity it is useful to measure the hydrogen-ion concentration of solutions. Hydrogen-ion concentrations are measured in moles per liter. A more widely used system is the pH scale.

The pH scale is used to express the hydrogen-ion concentration of aqueous solutions. Acidic solutions, having an hydrogen-ion concentration greater than 1×10^{-7} mol/L has a pH of less than 7. Basic solutions having a hydrogen-ion concentration less than 1×10^{-7} mol/L has a pH of greater than 7. Whereas neutral solutions have an hydrogen-ion concentration of exactly 1×10^{-7} mol/L with a pH equal to 7. Color changes of indicators can be related to specific pH values. Although most indicators are useful only over a pH range of approximately two units, red cabbage indicator has an effective range from pH = 2 to pH = 13.

Materials | Red cabbage indicator
Hydrochloric acid, 0.1 M, HCl (400 mL)
Sodium hydroxide, 0.1 M, NaOH (200 mL)
Ring stand with buret clamp
Buret (2)
600-mL Beaker
Magnetic stirrer and stir bar
150-mm Test tubes (6)
Test tube rack
10-mL pipet

Safety Precautions | Hydrochloric acid is highly toxic by ingestion and inhalation and severely corrosive to skin and eyes. Sodium hydroxide is caustic, corrosive to body tissue, and its solutions are very dangerous to eyes. Wear chemical splash goggles, chemical-resistant gloves and a chemical-resistant apron.

Preparation | Set up a buret clamped to a ring stand. Fill the buret with hydrochloric acid. Fill a 600-mL beaker with 200 mL sodium hydroxide and a few mL of the red cabbage indicator. The solution should be a yellow-green color. Insert a magnetic stirring bar into the beaker and place it onto a magnetic stirrer. Prepare a control by removing some of this solution and transferring it to a test tube. Label this test tube "1".

Demonstration

Position the buret over the beaker and open the stopcock to begin adding the hydrochloric acid to the sodium hydroxide solution. By adding the hydrochloric acid, the solution in the beaker should increase in acidity and the yellow-green color should change to green. At this point stop the flow of acid into the beaker. Transfer some of this solution to a second test tube and label this tube "2". Continue these steps, stopping at each color change, until the final red color of the indicator is observed. As acid is drained from the buret it will need to be filled periodically.

Once a color range is established, it is used to identify relative hydrogen-ion concentrations of solutions with unknown concentration. These color changes along with their identifying numbers can be used as a sort of modified pH scale. Unknowns can now be tested against this scale to identify their "red cabbage scale pH".

Disposal

The dilute solutions can be combined and flushed down the drain with excess water.

Acid Strength versus Concentration

Show the difference between acid strength, acid concentration and acid equivalence.

Application | Acids and Bases • Solutions • Molarity • Titration

Theory | The concepts of acid concentration (as expressed by molarity), acid equivalence (as determined by titration), and acid strength (as expressed by pH), are sometimes confused. This demonstration illustrates that these are three different properties of acids. The concentration (molarity) of an acid is simply an expression of how to prepare the solution. It indicates how much acid must be used to make the solution. The equivalence of an acid solution is an expression of how much base is required to neutralize it. This depends on the concentration of the acid and the number of acidic hydrogens on the acid molecule. The pH of an acid solution depends not only on the concentration and the equivalence, but also on the degree of ionization of the particular acid in the solution.

This demonstration uses hydrochloric, sulfuric, and acetic acids in equal concentration to demonstrate that their equivalencies and pH are all different. All acids are 0.1 M in concentration. The 0.1 M sulfuric acid and 0.1 M hydrochloric acid both have pH of approximately 1, but 0.1 M acetic acid has a pH of about 3. The acid strength of sulfuric and hydrochloric acids are therefore similar and stronger than acetic acid. Titration with sodium hydroxide shows that hydrochloric acid and acetic acid take about the same volume of sodium hydroxide solution for neutralization, while the sulfuric acid takes about twice as much. The equivalence is different due to the presence of two acidic hydrogens in the sulfuric acid molecule versus only one in acetic and hydrochloric acids.

Materials | Hydrochloric acid, 0.1 M, HCl (40 mL)
Sulfuric acid, 0.1 M, H_2SO_4 (40 mL)
Acetic acid, 0.1 M, $HC_2H_3O_2$ (40 mL)
Sodium hydroxide, 0.1 M, $NaOH$ (200 mL)
Phenolphthalein indicator (2 mL)
250-mL Beakers (3)
Pipet
Glass stirring rods (3)
pH meter or pH indicating paper
100-mL Graduated cylinder or buret
Labels for the beakers

Safety Precautions | Sulfuric acid, hydrochloric acid, and acetic acid are severely corrosive to eyes, skin, and other tissue and toxic by ingestion and inhalation. When making solutions, always add acid to water, never the reverse; considerable heat of dilution will occur.

Sodium hydroxide is a corrosive solid and skin burns are possible. Significant heat evolves when added to water and even dilute solutions are very dangerous to eyes and skin.

Wear chemical splash goggles, chemical-resistant gloves and a chemical-resistant apron.

Preparation

Prepare (see page A) or purchase the solutions. Label the three beakers with the names and concentrations of the acids.

Demonstration

Pour 40 mL of the appropriate acid into each beaker. Add 10 drops of phenolphthalein indicator to each beaker and stir the mixtures thoroughly. Use the pH meter or the pH test paper to test the pH of each acid solution. The HCl and H_2SO_4 will have a pH of about 1 and the $HC_2H_3O_2$ will be about 3. Record the pH values. While stirring the HCl solution, slowly pour 0.1 M NaOH solution from the 100-mL graduated cylinder or buret until the phenolphthalein indicator turns from colorless to pink. The volume of NaOH solution required to do this will be about 40 mL. Record the volume. Repeat this procedure with the beaker of sulfuric acid, and then with the beaker of acetic acid. The acetic acid will use about 40 mL, but the sulfuric acid will use about 80 mL of the NaOH.

Disposal

The dilute solutions can be combined and flushed down the drain with excess water.

Reference

Shakashiri, B. Z. *Chemical Demonstrations;* University of Wisconsin: Madison, WI, 1988; Vol. 3, p 137.

Amphoteric Substances

Show the amphoteric properties of some metallic hydroxides.

Application | Acids and Bases • Amphoteric Properties

Theory | A substance that reacts with either an acid or a base, that is, acting as an acid in the presence of a base and as a base when in the presence of an acid, is said to be amphoteric. Water is a classic example of an amphoteric substance, being able to accept protons from acids and form hydronium ions or to donate protons to bases and form hydroxide ions. Some metallic hydroxides, such as those of zinc, aluminum, chromium, and lead also exhibit amphoteric properties. In this demonstration, the amphoteric nature of zinc hydroxide will be shown. Zinc hydroxide, $Zn(OH)_2$, is only slightly soluble, and will precipitate from a solution of zinc nitrate when sodium hydroxide is added. If an excess of the sodium hydroxide is added, the zinc hydroxide will react, forming a soluble hydroxo complex. The reaction is:

$$Zn(OH)_2(s) + 2\ OH^-(aq) \rightarrow Zn(OH)_4^{2-}(aq)$$

In this reaction, zinc hydroxide acts as a Lewis acid, an electron pair acceptor.

Similarly, zinc hydroxide will dissolve in nitric acid solution, forming a hydrated complex. The reaction is:

$$Zn(OH)_2(s) + 2\ H^+(aq) + 2\ H_2O(l) \rightarrow Zn(H_2O)_4^{2+}(aq)$$

In this reaction, zinc hydroxide acts like a Lewis base, a proton acceptor.

Materials | Overhead projector
Zinc nitrate, 0.1 M, $Zn(NO_3)_2$ (40 mL)
Sodium hydroxide, 1.0 M, NaOH (20 mL)
Nitric acid, 1.0 M, HNO_3 (10 mL)
10-cm Petri dishes (2)
10-mL Graduated cylinders (2)

Safety Precautions | Nitric acid is corrosive; strong oxidant; toxic by inhalation; avoid contact with acetic acid and readily oxidized substances. Sodium hydroxide is a corrosive solid and skin burns are possible; even dilute solutions are very dangerous to eyes and skin. Zinc nitrate solid is moderately toxic by ingestion and a strong oxidant. Wear chemical splash goggles, chemical-resistant gloves and a chemical-resistant apron.

Preparation | Prepare the solutions. Zinc nitrate is prepared by dissolving 3.0 g $Zn(NO_3)_2 \cdot 6H_2O$ and 1 mL of 0.1 M nitric acid in 60 mL of distilled water, dilute the resulting solution to a volume of 100 mL. Sodium hydroxide is prepared by adding 4.0 g NaOH in sufficient distilled water to make 100 mL of solution. Nitric acid is prepared by adding 6.3 mL of concentrated reagent to 60 mL of distilled water, dilute the resulting solution to a volume of 100 mL. Pour 20 mL of the 0.1 M $Zn(NO_3)_2$ solution into each of the two Petri dishes.

Demonstration Set the Petri dishes on the overhead projector. Add 5 mL of 1 M NaOH to each dish and swirl gently to mix their contents. A precipitate of zinc hydroxide will form in each dish, darkening the image of each. To one of the dishes, add an additional 10 mL of 1 M NaOH and swirl the dish. The precipitate will redissolve after the second addition of the sodium hydroxide. To the other dish, add 8 mL of 1 M HNO_3 and swirl the dish gently. The precipitate in the second dish will also dissolve and the projected image will become clear after the nitric acid is added.

Disposal The waste solutions may be flushed down the drain with an excess of water.

Reference Shakashiri, B. Z. *Chemical Demonstrations;* University of Wisconsin: Madison, WI, 1988; Vol. 3, p 133.

Buffer Activity

Contrast the behavior of water and a buffer when acid or base is added.

Application   Acids and Bases • Equilibrium • Le Chatelier's Principle

Theory   The buffering action of a pH 7 buffer is caused by the presence of dihydrogen phosphate ion, $H_2PO_4^-$. The ion is hydrolyzed in solution and exists in equilibrium according to the following equation:

$$H_2PO_4^- + H_2O \rightleftarrows H_3O^+ + HPO_4^{2-}$$

Addition of acid drives the equilibrium to the left, while addition of base will drive the equilibrium to the right. Thus, the buffer is better able to resist changes in pH than ordinary water.

The buffering agent in Alka-Seltzer™ is the citrate ion, $H_2C_6H_5O_7^-$. The hydrolysis equilibrium is similar to the one shown above.

Materials   Distilled or deionized water
pH 7 Buffer, or KH_2PO_4
Universal indicator
Hydrochloric acid, 0.1 M, HCl
Sodium hydroxide, 0.1 M, NaOH
6-well Micro plate
Overhead projector
Alka-Seltzer cold medicine tablet

Safety Precautions   Solid sodium hydroxide is a corrosive solid; skin burns are possible; even dilute solutions are very dangerous to eyes and skin. Hydrochloric acid is highly toxic by ingestion or inhalation; severely corrosive to skin and eyes. Wear chemical splash goggles, chemical-resistant gloves and a chemical-resistant apron.

Preparation   The day before the demo, prepare the pH 7 buffer: dissolve 6.8 g KH_2PO_4 in 500 mL water, add 296 mL of 0.1 M NaOH, and dilute to a total volume of 1 liter, or order from Flinn Scientific (B0092).

Demonstration   Add 10 mL of distilled or deionized water to three wells of a 6-well micro plate on an overhead projector. Be sure to check the pH of the water beforehand, and adjust if necessary by adding small amounts of dilute sodium carbonate solution. Add 10 mL of the pH 7 buffer to each of the three other wells. Small beakers or Petri dishes could also be used. Add three or four drops of the Universal indicator to each sample. Now add one drop of 0.1 M HCl solution to one of the water samples. Add one drop of the HCl to one of the buffer samples. Continue adding acid dropwise to the buffer, counting the drops, until the buffer solution becomes the same color as the solution of water and HCl. Repeat the procedure, this time using 0.1 M NaOH solution. Then discuss the action of the buffer.

Dissolve an Alka-Seltzer cold medicine tablet in 100 mL of water. Add 10 mL of the resulting solution to three new wells. Add Universal indicator as before. Note the pH of the solution according to the indicator. Repeat the dropwise addition of the HCl and NaOH solutions as before. Compare the buffering capacity of the pH 2 buffer to the Alka-Seltzer.

Disposal

The dilute solutions can be flushed down the drain with excess water.

Reference

Kathleen Dombrink, McCluer North High School, Florissant, MO 63033.

Neutralization of Stomach Acid

An antacid tablet demonstrates how solubility is used to control reaction rate.

Application	Kinetics • Acids and Bases • Solubility • Equilibrium • pH
Theory	The antacid in Milk of Magnesia® tablets is magnesium hydroxide. This is a compound which is only slightly soluble ($K_{sp} = 8.9 \times 10^{-12}$) in water. This limited solubility means that the neutralization reaction can only proceed at a relatively slow rate, since the rate is restricted by the hydroxide ion concentration in the system. The dissolution process continues due to the destruction of the hydroxide ion in neutralization. The relevant reactions are:

$$\text{Dissolving: } Mg(OH)_2(s) \rightleftarrows Mg^{2+}(aq) + 2\ OH^-(aq)$$

$$\text{Neutralization: } 2H_3O^+(aq) + 2OH^-(aq) \rightleftarrows 4H_2O(l)$$

	The slow change in hydronium ion concentration is shown by the color change in the Universal indicator.
Materials	Phillips Milk of Magnesia tablet (1) Universal indicator (1 mL) 600-mL Beaker Distilled or deionized water Hydrochloric acid, 1 M, HCl Dropper pipet Magnetic stirrer and stir bar
Safety Precautions	Hydrochloric acid is highly toxic by ingestion or inhalation; severely corrosive to skin and eyes. Wear chemical splash goggles, chemical-resistant gloves and a chemical-resistant apron.
Preparation	Prepare (see page A) or purchase hydrochloric acid solution.
Demonstration	Place 300 mL of distilled water, 1 mL of the Universal indicator and 6 drops of 1 M HCl into the beaker, set on the magnetic stirrer, and begin stirring. Drop in the Milk of Magnesia tablet and observe.
Disposal	The solution can be flushed down the drain with excess water.
Reference	The Science Teacher **1981,** *48*(6), 53.

Common Ion Effect

Demonstrate the common ion effect using an indicator.

Application | Acids and Bases • Equilibrium • Buffers • pH • Le Chatelier's Principle

Theory | Weak acids such as acetic acid are only slightly dissociated in solution. The reaction can be viewed as an equilibrium:

$$HC_2H_3O_2 \rightleftarrows H^+ + C_2H_3O_2^-$$

Adding a soluble salt that contains a common ion, e.g. sodium acetate, will increase the concentration of the acetate ion, causing the equilibrium to shift toward the left. This will reduce the concentration of hydrogen ion and raise the pH (less acidic) of the solution. An indicator that shows a color change between the original and final pH of the system is used to show this visually.

Materials | Acetic acid, 0.15% solution, $HC_2H_3O_2$
Methyl red indicator
Sodium acetate, $NaC_2H_3O_2$
250-mL Beaker
Stirring rod
Overhead projector

Safety Precautions | Glacial acetic acid is corrosive to skin and tissue, toxic by ingestion, and a moderate fire risk (flash point 39 °C). Sodium acetate is a skin, eye and respiratory irritant. Wear chemical splash goggles, chemical-resistant gloves and a chemical-resistant apron.

Preparation | Prepare the 0.15% acetic acid solution by adding 1.5 mL glacial acetic acid to approximately 1 liter of water. Prepare the methyl red indicator by dissolving 0.02 g methyl red in 60 mL of 95% ethanol then add 40 mL of distilled water.

Demonstration | Put 100 mL of the acid solution in the beaker and place it on the overhead projector. Add a few drops of the methyl red indicator and stir. The solution will have a red color. Add about 1 gram of solid sodium acetate to the beaker and stir. The solution will change toward a more yellow color. The pH transition range for methyl red is 4.4 red to 6.2 yellow.

Disposal | The solution can be flushed down the drain with excess water.

Reference | Adapted from Metcalfe, et al. *Exercises and Experiments in Modern Chemistry;* Holt, Rinehart, Winston: Orlando, FL, 1986; p 224.

Electrolytic Titration

A conductivity meter is used to show the equivalence point of a titration.

Application | Acids and Bases • Titration • Conductivity • Neutralization

Theory | The reaction between sulfuric acid and barium hydroxide produces a precipitate of barium sulfate. As the equivalence point of the titration is neared, the ion concentration in the solution gets very low because the barium sulfate has precipitated, and the other product is water. Conductivity of an electrolyte is a function of ion concentration. Since barium sulfate has a K_{sp} of 1.5×10^{-9}, when precipitation is complete, the remaining barium ion concentration is approximately 3.8×10^{-5} mol/L and the hydroxide ion concentration is 7.7×10^{-5} mol/L, for a pH of 9.8. Phenolphthalein changes color at pH 8 to 10. The usual result is that the light bulb goes out just before the phenolphthalein color change occurs. The neutral point of this titration is at pH 7. If additional acid is added after the equivalence point, the ion concentrations in the solution rise rapidly and the conductivity apparatus again glows brightly. On some occasions, depending on the size of the bulb in the conductivity apparatus, the color change might occur before the bulb goes out.

Materials | Sulfuric acid, 1 M, H_2SO_4 (50 mL)
Barium hydroxide, saturated solution, $Ba(OH)_2$ (200 mL)
Conductivity apparatus
250-mL Beaker
Ring stand
Buret
Buret clamp
Phenolphthalein indicator
Magnetic stirrer (optional)

Safety Precautions | Sulfuric acid is severely corrosive to eyes, skin and other tissue; considerable heat of dilution with water; even very dilute solutions are harmful to eyes and skin. Barium hydroxide is a strong base and corrosive. Barium compounds are toxic by ingestion. Wear chemical splash goggles and always follow laboratory safety rules while performing demonstrations.

Preparation | Prepare the barium hydroxide solution by dissolving 8 g in 200 mL of distilled water, stir then filter.

Demonstration | Fill the buret with the sulfuric acid and zero. Place the buret in a clamp and position the buret tip over the 250-mL beaker. Set the beaker on the magnetic stirrer and add the spinbar. (If you don't have a magnetic stirrer, no problem, use a stirring rod.) Add the barium hydroxide solution to the beaker. Add a few drops of phenolphthalien to give a persistent pink color. Lower the conductivity apparatus into the solution and turn it on. Begin adding the sulfuric acid from the buret. The solution will begin to turn cloudy. As more acid is added, the solution gets more clouded, and eventually the bulb of the conductivity apparatus starts to dim. Slow down the acid delivery to one drop at a time. The lightbulb goes out, and shortly after, the color fades. If additional acid is added, the lightbulb comes on again and glows brightly.

Disposal   Filter and dry the barium sulfate precipitate, place in a plastic container and dispose in a suitable landfill according to Flinn Suggested Disposal Method #27h. The liquid solutions may be flushed down the drain with excess water.

Reference   Summerlin, L., et al. *Chemical Demonstrations;* American Chemical Society: Washington, DC, 1988; Vol. 2, pp 130–131.

Indicator Sponge

Use this as a checkup on student lab techniques.

Application	Acids and Bases • Indicators • Lab Safety
Theory	A cellulose sponge treated with Congo red indicator becomes a permanent, reusable indicator. The indicator color transition is between pH 3.0 (blue) and 5.0 (red). A drop of acid solution on a desktop will change the indicator from red to blue immediately. The color can be regenerated by rinsing the sponge in a sodium bicarbonate solution.
Materials	Cellulose sponge, light color Congo red indicator Distilled or deionized water Sodium bicarbonate, saturated solution, $NaHCO_3$ Acetic or hydrochloric acid, 1 M
Safety Precautions	Acid solutions are corrosive to eyes, skin and other tissue. Wear chemical splash goggles, chemical-resistant gloves and a chemical-resistant apron.
Preparation	Make a solution of 1 g of the Congo red indicator in about 100 mL of distilled or deionized water. Soak the dry sponge in this solution, periodically squeezing out the liquid. Wear rubber gloves to keep from staining hands. Let the sponge stand in the liquid overnight. Squeeze out as much liquid as possible and let dry completely. Rinse with fresh water a few times and the indicator sponge is ready to use.
Demonstration	Place a drop or two of acid solution onto the sponge. Show students the color change. Treat the blue spots with a small amount of sodium bicarbonate solution to regenerate the red color. This demo can be used early in the school year, when students are sometimes careless about cleaning up spills on the lab bench. If there has been an acid spill on a student bench, the visual impact of the color change in the sponge should get the safety lesson across.
Disposal	Save the sponge and flush the solutions down the drain with excess water.
Reference	George Dobush, Montclair State College, New Jersey.

Hydrolysis of the Carbonate Ion

Introduce students to the concept of hydrolysis of ions in aqueous solution.

Application | Acids and Bases • Conjugate Pairs • Hydrolysis • Weak Acids

Theory | The reaction between aqueous solutions of cupric nitrate and sodium carbonate provides an excellent demonstration of the concept of hydrolysis of an acid/base conjugate pair. Mixing the two solutions produces a blue precipitate. The precipitate is cupric hydroxide, not cupric carbonate. The presence of hydroxide ions in the carbonate solution is explained by the hydrolysis of the carbonate ion. The reaction is:

$$CO_3^{2-}(aq) + H_2O(1) \rightarrow HCO_3^-(aq) + OH^-(aq)$$

Materials | Cupric carbonate, $CuCO_3$
Cupric nitrate, 0.1 M, $Cu(NO_3)_2$ (20 mL)
Sodium carbonate, 0.1 M, Na_2CO_3 (10 mL)
Sodium hydroxide, 0.1 M, NaOH (10 mL)
Test tubes (3)

Safety Precautions | Cupric nitrate is moderately toxic, an oxidizing material and dangerous in contact with organic materials. Sodium carbonate may be a skin irritant.

Sodium hydroxide is a corrosive solid; skin burns are possible; solutions are very dangerous to eyes and skin. Wear chemical splash goggles, chemical-resistant gloves and a chemical-resistant apron.

Preparation | Prepare or purchase solutions:

0.1 M Cupric nitrate; 2.41 g $Cu(NO_3)_2 \cdot 3H_2O$ per 100 mL of solution.
0.1 M Sodium carbonate; 1.06 g Na_2CO_3 per 100 mL of solution.
0.1 M Sodium hydroxide; 0.40 g NaOH per 100 mL of solution.
Label test tubes 1, 2, 3.

Demonstration | In test tube 1, mix 10 mL of $Cu(NO_3)_2$ and 10 mL of Na_2CO_3 solutions. Ask for statements from students about the possible identity of the precipitate. Add 20 mL of water to test tube 2 and 1 g of $CuCO_3$. Mix thoroughly. Ask students to compare the two tubes.

Pour 10 mL of $Cu(NO_3)_2$ solution into tube 3. Add 10 mL of NaOH solution and mix. Display all three tubes and discuss the results. Most students initially identify the precipitate in tube 1 as $CuCO_3$. Demonstration 2 shows this is questionable. Demonstration 3 shows that the precipitate in tube 1 is more like $Cu(OH)_2$. This could only have been formed by the hydrolysis of the carbonate ion as shown above.

Disposal | Solutions can be flushed down the sink with excess water.

Reference | Walker, N. and Mintz, J. *J. Chem Ed.* **1970,** *47,* A119

Chapter 14

Kinetics

The Effect of Temperature on Reaction Rate

Varying the temperature will effect the rate of reaction.

Application	Temperature • Kinetics
Theory	As the temperature of the reactants is increased, the products are formed at a faster rate. The reaction of Alka Seltzer™ with water produces a gas, carbon dioxide which fills the balloon faster at a higher temperature.
Materials	250-mL Erlenmeyer flasks (3) Alka Seltzer tablets (3) Balloons (3) Water
Safety Precautions	Be particularly careful heating the water and placing the balloon over the hot flask. Wear chemical splash goggles and always follow laboratory safety rules while performing demonstrations.
Preparation	Prepare equal amounts of water, 75 to 100 mL, at 0, 20 and 90 °C.
Demonstration	Ask for three student volunteers. Add about 75 mL of water to each of three 250-mL Erlenmeyer flasks. One flask should be a 0 °C, the second should be at room temperature and the third at about 90 °C. Have each volunteer put an Alka Seltzer tablet into a different colored balloon. Have the volunteers place their balloons over the top of their flasks, holding on to the Alka Seltzer tablet through the balloon. Instruct them to drop the tablets into the flasks simultaneously. Initially, the size of the balloons will be proportional to the temperature but after about 20 minutes the sizes of the balloons will equalize because the amount of product produced in each case is the same, only the rates are different.
Disposal	Solution can be flushed down the drain with excess water.

Entropy as a Driving Force

Demonstrate the role of entropy as a driving force for spontaneous change.

Application	Gas Laws • Thermodynamics
Theory	When a piece of rubber is stretched, it becomes warmer, and when it is allowed to relax, it becomes cooler. The warming is attributed to the fact that work is done on the system as the rubber is stretched, and some of this work results in an increase in thermal energy of the rubber. The cooling is due to the work that is done by the rubber as it contracts. The energy to do this work must come from the internal thermal energy of the rubber. In order for a process to be spontaneous, the entropy of the universe must increase. The contraction of the rubber is spontaneous, so the final, shorter, cooled state has resulted in a heat transfer to the surroundings which increases the entropy. The process is essentially adiabatic due to the speed with which it occurs.
Materials	Latex balloons, 1 per student (or wide rubber bands).
Safety Precautions	Wear chemical splash goggles and always follow laboratory safety rules while performing demonstrations.
Preparation	None required.
Demonstration	Pass out balloons to each student in the class. Have students slip the balloon onto an index finger up to about the knuckle joint. The neck of the balloon should be held with the thumb of the same hand. Taking the rest of the balloon with the other hand, stretch it rapidly. After pausing a moment, allow it to contract rapidly. Students will notice the effect without being coached. As the balloon is stretched, the finger becomes warmed, and upon contraction, the finger is cooled. Repeat the cycle a few times to contrast the two effects. Heavier material in the balloon construction will give a more pronounced warming and cooling.
Alternate Procedure	Stretch a rubber band tight, hold against upper lip, sense heat. Remove from lip, relax, touch lip with relaxed band, sense coolness.
Disposal	None required.
Reference	Salzsieder, J. C. *J. Chem. Ed.* **1981**, *58*, 280.

Brominating Acetone

Bromine is reacted with acetone under various conditions and reaction times are recorded.

Application

Organic Chemistry • Kinetics • Equilibrium

Theory

In the presence of hydrochloric acid, bromine added to acetone turns colorless. The reaction, which produces bromoacetone and HBr, is:

$$CH_3CCH_3 + Br_2 \rightarrow BrCH_2CCH_3 + HBr$$

Bromoacetone

Reaction variables may be evaluated by changing concentrations and temperature and by measuring reaction times by observing disappearance of color.

Materials

Acetone, CH_3COCH_3 (325 mL)
Hydrochloric acid, 2 M, HCl (700 mL)
Bromine water, 0.01 M, Br_2(aq) (650 mL)
600-mL Beakers, (7)
Distilled water
Magnetic stirrer
Clock (stopwatch)

Preparation

Prepare the following solutions:

Solution A: 700 mL 8 M acetone; dilute 324.8 g acetone in water to make 700 mL total solution.

Solution B: 700 mL 2 M HCl; dilute 116 mL 12 M HCl with enough water to make 700 mL total solution.

Solution C: 650 mL 0.01 M Br_2(aq); add 15 drops bromine to 650 mL of distilled water or 65 mL bromine water diluted to 650 mL.

Safety Precautions

Exercise extreme caution when handling bromine. Bromine is highly toxic by inhalation and ingestion; severe skin irritant; very strong oxidizer; reacts violently with many organic compounds. Sodium thiosulfate solution (0.1 M) should be available as a neutralizer for bromine in the event of an accident. Hydrochloric acid is highly toxic by ingestion or inhalation; severely corrosive to skin and eyes. Acetone is flammable, a dangerous fire risk and toxic by ingestion and inhalation. Wear chemical splash goggles, chemical-resistant gloves and a chemical-resistant apron.

Demonstration	**Reference Reaction:** Mix 100 mL solution A, 100 mL solution B, and 100 mL distilled water. Add 100 mL solution C. Stir and begin timing at the addition of solution C.
	Acetone Excess Reaction: Mix 200 mL solution A with 100 mL solution B. Add 100 mL solution C. Stir and begin timing at the addition of solution C.
	Acid Excess Reaction: Mix 100 mL solution A with 200 mL solution B. Add 100 mL solution C. Stir and begin timing at the addition of solution C.
	Temperature Effect: Mix 100 mL solution A, 100 mL solution B, and 100 mL distilled water. Heat mixture to 40 °C. Add 100 mL solution C. Stir and begin timing at the addition of solution C.
	Bromine Concentration Reactions: Mix 100 mL solution A with 100 mL solution B. Add 200 mL solution C. Stir and time, beginning at the addition of solution C.
	Mix 100 mL solution A, 100 mL solution B, and 150 mL distilled water. Add 50 mL solution C. Stir and begin timing at the addition of solution C.
	Note: This demo can be halved and performed in a 400 mL beaker.
Disposal	Because the waste is a mixture of reagents, disposal should be done in two steps: first, evaporation, (Flinn Suggested Disposal Method #18a), followed by neutralization, (Flinn Suggested Disposal Method #24b).
Reference	Bruce Gray, University of Pittsburgh, Dept. of Chemistry.

The Exploding Flask

Exothermic combustion of alcohol is catalyzed by precious metals.

Application Catalysts • Thermochemistry

Theory Certain metals such as platinum and palladium catalyze the vapor phase oxidation of alcohols. The oxidation reaction that occurs produces intermittent explosions. The period and loudness of the explosions depend on the catalyst, the alcohol and the size of the flask. The explosion is due to the exothermic combustion of the alcohol or aldehyde which is ignited by the red hot metal.

The platinum or palladium metal is an effective catalyst for the oxidation of alcohols to aldehydes or ketones. When ethanol is oxidized, the products are acetaldehyde and hydrogen and the reaction is endothermic; requiring an input of heat. This oxidation can also be described as a dehydrogenation reaction.

The heat for the oxidation reaction comes from the subsequent oxidation of hydrogen at the catalyst surface, which is exothermic.

$$CH_3CH_2OH \xrightarrow{[Pt]} CH_3CHO + H_2 \quad \Delta H° = +16.5 \text{ kcal/mol}$$
$$H_2 + \tfrac{1}{2}O_2 \rightarrow H_2O \quad\quad\quad\quad \Delta H° = -57.8 \text{ kcal/mol}$$
$$CH_3CH_2OH + 2\tfrac{1}{2}O_2 \rightarrow CO_2 + 3H_2O \quad \Delta H° = -56.2 \text{ kcal/mol}$$
$$CH_3CHO + 3O_2 \rightarrow 2CO_2 + 2H_2O \quad \Delta H° = -39.7 \text{ kcal/mol}$$

Materials 1000-mL Erlenmeyer flask
Steel or Aluminum divider
Palladium or Platinum wire (30 cm)
Ethanol
Hot plate
Bunsen burner

Safety Precautions Ethanol is flammable and a dangerous fire risk; addition of denaturant makes the ethanol poisonous. The apparatus gets very hot! Handle with care using gloves or a pot holder. Have a fire extinguisher readily available. Acetaldehyde is produced, so ensure proper ventilation or perform in a hood.

An initial explosion may occur as the wire is put into place. Be aware of this! Wear chemical splash goggles, chemical-resistant gloves and a chemical-resistant apron.

Preparation Use an Erlenmeyer flask. Construct a steel divider as follows:

Prepare the catalyst by coiling the Pt or Pd wire and attatching the other end to a stir rod. The coil should hang about halfway down the flask.

The divider should be just the diameter of the flask neck if the fan type is not used. It must touch the bottom and extend several cm above the top.

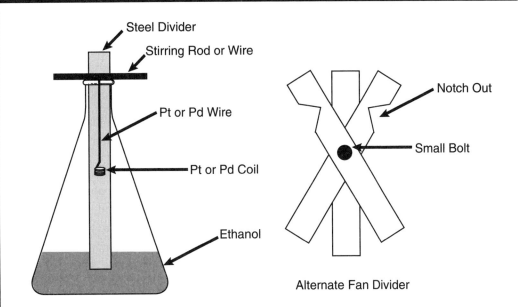

Steel Divider

Stirring Rod or Wire

Pt or Pd Wire

Pt or Pd Coil

Ethanol

Notch Out

Small Bolt

Alternate Fan Divider

Demonstration

Introduce 50 to 75 mL ethanol and heat it to boiling in the flask. This ensures enough vapor to start the reaction. Heating should only be done on a hot plate.

Heat the coil of wire to glowing with a burner — keep open flames away from flask and quickly suspend it in the flask. An initial explosion may occur, but will be followed within seconds to one minute by successive explosions. If two or more minutes pass without explosions, re-heat the coil. If this fails the alcohol may have cooled or there may not be enough air. Correct for these by heating or blowing air into the flask carefully.

Keep all open flames at a safe distance! If the alcohol ignites at the mouth of the flask—snuff out the flames with a damp towel.

Disposal

Evaporate the alcohol to dryness or flush down a sink with copious amounts of water.

References

R. Battinno, Wright State University, Dayton, OH.
T. Letcher, Rhodes University, Grahamestown 6140, South Africa.

Inhibition of Hydrogen Peroxide

An inhibitor is used to slow the decomposition of hydrogen peroxide.

Application | Catalysis • Inhibitors • Kinetics • Hydrogen Peroxide

Theory | A substance that interferes with catalysis is an inhibitor. Practically anything will cause hydrogen peroxide to decompose into water and oxygen gas:

$$H_2O_2(aq) \rightarrow H_2O(g) + \frac{1}{2}O_2(g)$$

Even dust particles and scratched or dirty glass containers will increase the rate of decomposition. To prevent decomposition during shipping and to prolong shelf life, manufacturers of hydrogen peroxide may add phosphate ion to slow the process. In this demonstration iron (III) nitrate acts as a catalyst that increases the rate of decomposition:

$$2H_2O_2 + Fe(NO_3)_3 \rightarrow 2H_2O + O_2 + Fe^{3+} + 3NO_3^-$$

whereas sodium phosphate serves as an inhibitor of the catalytic reaction:

$$Fe^{3+} + PO_4^{3-} \rightarrow FePO_4(s)$$

Materials | Hydrogen peroxide, 30% solution, H_2O_2 (15–25 mL)
1-L Florence flask
Ferric nitrate, 0.1 M, $Fe(NO_3)_3 \cdot 9H_2O$ (1 mL)
Sodium phosphate, tribasic, 0.1 M, $Na_3PO_4 \cdot 12H_2O$ (1 mL)
Pipet

Safety Precautions | Hydrogen peroxide is severely corrosive to the skin, eyes and respiratory tract; a very strong oxidant; a dangerous fire and explosion risk. Ferric nitrate is a strong oxidizer and a skin and tissue irritant. Sodium phosphate, tribasic is moderately toxic by ingestion and a skin irritant. Wear chemical splash goggles, chemical-resistant gloves and a chemical-resistant apron.

Preparation | Prepare solutions: Ferric nitrate (4 g in 100 mL water) and sodium phosphate, tribasic (3.8 g in 100 mL water).

Demonstration | Pour 15 to 25 mL hydrogen peroxide into a clean Florence flask. Add a few drops of ferric nitrate solution to the flask. The reaction will quickly develop producing enough heat energy to vaporize the water in the mixture. At this point add an equal number of drops of sodium phosphate solution. The reaction will be brought to a crashing halt.

Disposal | Finish decomposing the hydrogen peroxide with ferric nitrate before flushing down the drain with excess water.

Reference | George R. Gross, Union High School, Union, NJ.

Co-Catalysis

Two solutions are mixed and act as co-catalysts in decomposing a solution of hydrogen peroxide.

Application	Catalysis • Co-Catalysis • Kinetics • Hydrogen Peroxide • Decomposition
Theory	Cupric chloride and ferric chloride solutions both act as catalysts to increase the rate of the decomposition of hydrogen peroxide. When the two catalysts are mixed, the Cu^{2+} and the Fe^{3+} ions act together as co-catalysts and triple the rate of reaction.
Materials	Cupric chloride, 0.2 M, $CuCl_2 \cdot 2H_2O$ Ferric chloride, 1 M, $FeCl_3 \cdot 6H_2O$ Hydrogen peroxide, 6%, H_2O_2 100-mm Test tubes (3) 500-mL Erlenmeyer flasks (3) 10″ Balloons (3)
Safety Precautions	Hydrogen peroxide is severely corrosive to the skin, eyes and respiratory tract; it is a strong oxidant and a dangerous fire and explosion risk. Cupric chloride is toxic by ingestion and inhalation. Ferric chloride is a skin and tissue irritant, moderately toxic by ingestion, and corrosive. Wear chemical splash goggles, chemical-resistant gloves and a chemical-resistant apron.
Preparation	Prepare the cupric chloride solution by dissolving 3.5 g in 100 mL H_2O water and ferric chloride solution by dissolving 27.0 g in 100 mL H_2O. Purchase 6% H_2O_2 or prepare by adding 75 mL 30% H_2O_2 to 300 mL water just prior to demonstration. Introduce 100 mL of the 6% H_2O_2 solution into each of the three flasks. Label the flasks A, B and C. Add 5 mL of the cupric chloride solution and 5 mL distilled water into a test tube. Carefully slide this test tube into Flask A without spilling any of the contents into the flask. Add 5 mL of the ferric chloride solution and 5 mL distilled water. Slide this second test tube into Flask B. Add 5 mL of the cupric chloride solution and 5 mL of the ferric chloride solution into the last test tube. Slide this test tube into Flask C. Secure a balloon over the mouths of each of the three flasks.
Demonstration	Turn over each of the three flasks—allowing the contents of the test tubes to mix with the hydrogen peroxide solutions. Observe the rate at which the balloons expand.
Disposal	Solutions can be flushed down the drain with excess water.
Reference	Walton, J. H. *J. Chem. Ed.,* **1931,** *8,* 303.

Inhibiting Effects on Enzyme Activity

Catalase is an enzyme used to catalyze the decomposition of hydrogen peroxide but is inhibited when cupric ions are added to the reaction.

Application | Catalysis • Inhibition • Catalase • Decomposition • Hydrogen Peroxide

Theory | Catalase, an enzyme extracted from potatoes, rutabagas and turnips specifically catalyzes the decomposition of hydrogen peroxide into water and oxygen gas:

$$H_2O_2(aq) \xrightarrow{\text{catalase}} H_2O(l) + \tfrac{1}{2}O_2(g)$$

A solution of cupric sulfate is added to the catalase solution, which in turn inhibits the reaction. Catalase requires Fe^{2+} ions as an activator. The Cu^{2+} ions compete with the Fe^{2+} ions and prevent it from activating the catalase. The enzyme catalase present in blood is what causes the bubbling when H_2O_2 is used as a disinfectant for cuts.

Materials | Hydrogen peroxide, 10% solution, 5 H_2O_2 (75 mL)
Catalase solution
Cupric sulfate, 0.2 M, $CuSO_4 \cdot 5\ H_2O$
Distilled water
100-mm Test tubes (2)
500-mL Erlenmeyer flasks (2)
Balloons, 10-inch (2)

Safety Precautions | 30% hydrogen peroxide is severely corrosive to the skin, eyes and respiratory tract. It is a strong oxidant and a dangerous fire and explosion risk. Cupric sulfate is a skin and respiratory irritant; toxic by inhalation and ingestion. Wear chemical splash goggles, chemical-resistant gloves and a chemical-resistant apron.

Preparation | Peel and grind a potato, rutabaga or turnip in a blender with about 25 mL distilled water. Filter the solution and set aside. Prepare the hydrogen peroxide by diluting 25 mL of 30% H_2O_2 solution in enough water to make 75 mL solution. Cupric sulfate solution is prepared by dissolving 5 g $CuSO_4 \cdot 5\ H_2O$ in enough water to make 100 mL solution.

Demonstration | Pour 15 mL of hydrogen peroxide solution into each Erlenmeyer flask. Set aside. Pour 5 mL of catalase solution into two test tubes. Add 5 to 10 drops of cupric sulfate solution to one of the test tubes, label this test tube as the inhibitor.

Slide one test tube into one of the Erlenmeyer flasks and place a balloon over the mouth of the flask. Do the same with the other flask and test tube.

Invert the flasks to allow the contents of the test tubes to mix with the hydrogen peroxide solution. Observe that the reaction has been inhibited in the flask containing cupric ions.

Disposal	The solution can be flushed down the drain with excess water.
Reference	Summerlin, L. et al. *Chemical Demonstrations;* American Chemical Society: Washington, DC, 1988; Vol. 2, p 152.

Genie in a Bottle

Hydrogen peroxide is catalytically decomposed to produce a cloud.

Application | Catalysis • Decomposition • Hydrogen Peroxide

Theory | Hydrogen peroxide decomposes to form oxygen and water. This reaction is a slow reaction at room temperature. Catalysts speed up reactions. It is catalyzed by many substances including KI and the MnO_2 used here. The enzyme catalase present in blood is what causes the bubbling when H_2O_2 is used as a disinfectant for cuts. The exothermic reaction generates enough heat to produce large amounts of water vapor. Hence, the *Genie* effect.

Materials | *Magic Genie,* Flinn Demo Kit, AP2092
   or
1000-mL Kjeldahl or volumetric flask
Aluminum foil
Hydrogen peroxide, 30% solution, H_2O_2 (40 mL)
Tea bag or tissue paper
Thread or fine copper wire
Manganese dioxide, MnO_2 (1 g) or potassium iodide, KI (2 g)
1-hole Rubber stopper

Safety Precautions | Hydrogen peroxide is severely corrosive to the skin, eyes and respiratory tract; a very strong oxidant; and a dangerous fire and explosion risk. Manganese dioxide is a strong oxidant and moderately toxic. The reaction flask will get hot, use a Pyrex® flask. Wear chemical splash goggles, chemical-resistant gloves and a chemical-resistant apron.

Preparation | A Kjeldahl flask works well if you have one around. Volumetric flasks work equally well. Wrap the flask in foil to maintain the mystery.

Place 30 to 40 mL of 30% hydrogen peroxide carefully into the flask using a long stem funnel so no peroxide gets on the neck of the flask. Be certain the flask is secure from tipping over.

Prepare a "sachet" of about one gram of manganese dioxide, like a tea bag using tissue or toilet paper making sure none of the catalyst comes through the paper. Tie the bag with thread, string or fine wire.

Hang the bag in the top of the neck of the flask and hold it in place with a 1-hole rubber stopper. The stopper must have a hole in it—allowing the steam to escape in case a reaction occurs inadvertently.

Demonstration | Initiate the reaction by removing the stopper and permitting the bag to fall into the peroxide. The reaction may take a few seconds, be patient.

Disposal | The solution can be flushed down the drain with excess water.

Micro Grain Elevator

Demonstrate the principle of a grain elevator or flour mill explosion on a small scale.

Application	Kinetics • Solids • Surface Area • Reaction Rates • Explosions
Theory	Reactions involving solids can only occur at the surface of the solid. Dust explosions are common problems in coal mines, grain elevators, flour mills and sawmills because very finely ground solids are suspended in air—creating an explosive environment. The increased surface area of the fine powder causes the reaction rate to be dramatically increased if ignited.
Materials	*The Mini Grain Elevator Explosion,* Flinn Demo Kit, AP8729 or Corn starch, cake flour, sawdust, or lycopodium powder 1-quart Paint can with lid Short candle Pipet, thin stem
Safety Precautions	Lycopodium powder is easily combustible/explosive, especially when dispersed through the air. Be careful not to allow the powder to become airborne. Keep all flammable materials away from the demonstration area. Do not stand over the can when doing the demonstration. The lid will be propelled into the air with great force and a relatively large flame will be produced. Lycopodium powder may cause allergic reactions, and precautions should be taken not to let the powder get airborne. The other suggested materials will also work well if dry and should be handled with the same precautions. Wear chemical splash goggles and always follow laboratory safety rules while performing demonstrations.
Preparation	Use a nail to punch a hole in the side of the paint can about one inch from the top. The hole should be as close to the size of your pipette stem as possible. Place a short candle in the bottom of the paint can.
Demonstration	Squeeze the air out of the pipet. Lower the pipet into the container of powder and release the bulb to fill the pipet with the powder. The bulb should be about two-thirds full for best results. Light the candle and close the lid of the paint can. The tighter the lid, the bigger the boom—but use caution! Poke the tip of the pipet into the hole in the side of the can. Be sure that the powder is near the open end of the pipet. Tilt the pipet slightly upward and squeeze. The lid should explode off of the can.
Disposal	The can and candle are reusable. Any excess powder can be cleaned up with wet paper towels and disposed of in the trash.
Reference	Lee Marek, Naperville High School, Naperville, IL, Woodrow Wilson Chem 8 Institute.

Activated Complex

The action of a catalyst is illustrated by different colored activated complexes and products.

Application | Catalysis • Kinetics • Activated Complex

Theory | The reaction involves the oxidation of tartaric acid by hydrogen peroxide in the presence of a cobalt catalyst. The gas evolved is a mixture of carbon dioxide and oxygen. Oxalic acid is also produced. The catalyst, cobalt (II) chloride is pink in an aqueous solution, but when added to the tartrate–peroxide mixture, forms a green complex and quickly catalyzes the oxidation. This illustrates the role of an activated complex in a reaction mechanism.

As the tartrate is oxidized, the catalyst is r'egenerated and the solution returns to a pink color. If you wish to show temperature effects as well, time the reaction at different temperatures between 30 and 70 °C.

Materials | *Cobalt Chloride, "The Pink Catalyst",* Flinn demo kit AP2084
  or
Beaker
Graduated cylinders, 1 each 250-mL, 100-mL, 25-mL
Sodium potassium tartrate, 0.30 M, $NaKC_4H_4O_6 \cdot 4H_2O$
Hydrogen peroxide, 6% solution, H_2O_2
Cobalt (II) chloride solution, 0.3 M, $CoCl_2$
Hot plate
Thermometers

Safety Precautions | Hydrogen peroxide is severely corrosive to the skin, eyes, and respiratory tract; a very strong oxidant; and a dangerous fire and explosion risk. Cobalt (II) chloride is toxic by ingestion; causes blood damage.

If you decide to do runs at different temperatures, do not exceed 70 °C. At higher temperatures this reaction is very vigorous and will foam over the sides of the beaker. Wear chemical splash goggles, chemical-resistant gloves and a chemical-resistant apron.

Preparation | Prepare the sodium potassium tartrate solution by adding 84.6 g per liter of solution, and the cobalt (II) chloride solution by adding 7.14 g per 100 mL of solution.

Purchase 6% H_2O_2 solution or prepare by diluting 70 mL of 30% H_2O_2 to 350 mL with distilled water.

Demonstration	Add 200 mL of the tartrate solution and 65 mL of the peroxide solution to the large beaker. Cover with a watch glass and place the beaker on the hot plate and heat to 45 to 50 °C. While the mixture is heating, measure out 15 mL of the cobalt (II) chloride solution. When the mixture reaches temperature, remove the beaker from the hot plate and add the cobalt (II) chloride solution. Cover the beaker with the watch glass again. The pink solution turns green, and the reaction proceeds. A gas is evolved. The solution turns pink again and the reaction stops.
Disposal	Collect all solutions containing cobalt (II) chloride and dispose of according to Flinn Suggested Disposal Method #27f.
Reference	Ruda, P. T. *J. Chem. Ed.* **1978,** *55,* 652.

Dragon's Breath

Demonstrate the effect of surface area and particle size on reaction rates of solids.

Application | Kinetics • Reaction Rates • Explosions • Solids

Theory | Reactions involving solids can only occur at the surface of the solid. Dust explosions are common problems in coal mines, grain elevators, flour mills and sawmills. The increased surface area of the fine powder causes the reaction rate to be dramatically increased.

Materials | Bunsen burner
3/8-inch Tygon tubing, (1 m)
Small funnel
Cake flour, very fine sawdust, or lycopodium powder.

Safety Precautions | Be careful with open flames. Very fine solids such as cake flour or sawdust are very flammable and an explosion risk; do not point the opening of the tube toward audience. Lycopodium powder can cause an allergic reaction in some individuals. Wear chemical splash goggles and always follow laboratory safety rules while performing demonstrations.

Preparation | Using the funnel, introduce about a teaspoonful of the flour or sawdust into one end of the Tygon tubing. The wood residue from sandpapering operations is excellent. A potential source might be companies that make furniture or cabinets or your school's wood shop.

Demonstration | Light the burner. Hold the filled end of the Tygon tubing about 10 cm to the side and about 10 cm above the top of the burner flame. Blow sharply through the tube to expel the flour as a fine cloud. Don't inhale! It will ignite into a fireball that is about 60 cm in diameter lasting for about 0.25 sec. Do not blow towards students.

Disposal | Any unburned residue can be swept up and discarded in the trash.

Reference | Lee Marek, Naperville High School, Naperville, IL, at Woodrow Wilson Chem 8 Institute.

Burning Iron

Show the importance of surface area to reaction rates.

Application | Kinetics • Chemical Changes • Solids • Redox

Theory | Most students do not consider the importance of surface area to the reaction rate of a solid. Thus, if asked "can iron burn?", the usual response is "no!". However, if a solid can be divided finely enough, the enormous increase in surface area allows a rapid oxidation to occur. The reaction is:

$$4\,Fe(s) + 3\,O_2(g) \rightarrow 2\,Fe_2O_3(s)$$

The oxide has a bluish gray color, rather than the typical rust color. This may be attributed to the lack of any water of hydration in the solid.

Materials | Steel wool, very fine
Acetone
150-mL Beaker
9 V battery (use a fresh one)
Zip-lock® bag

Safety Precautions | Acetone is flammable, a dangerous fire risk, and toxic by inhalation and ingestion. Use only with proper ventilation and keep away from any open flame or ignition source. Remove all flammable material from demonstration area. Wear chemical splash goggles, chemical-resistant gloves and a chemical-resistant apron.

Preparation | Soak the steel wool in acetone for 15 to 20 minutes. Remove and allow to dry overnight under the fume hood. The purpose of this is to remove the oil or plastic coating that is usually present on steel wool to prevent rusting.

Demonstration | Determine the mass of a small piece of the steel wool in the plastic bag. Unwrap the steel wool, pulling the strands apart as far as practical to get maximum surface exposure. Hang the pulled apart steel wool from a clamp on a ring stand. Ignite the steel wool by touching the battery contacts to the steel wool. It will burn readily, which surprises most students. After about two minutes, the solid residue can be safely handled. Place it back in the bag and determine its mass. Ask students to predict if it will be greater or less. They will usually say less, thinking about the ash of a combustion. Someone might predict no change due to conservation of mass. The mass actually increases due to the addition of oxygen.

Disposal | The steel wool can be discarded in the trash.

Reference | Penney Sconzo, The Westminster School, Atlanta, GA, at Woodrow Wilson TORCH program, Chem 2.

Lightstick Kinetics

Show students the relationship between reaction rates and temperature.

Application | Kinetics • Reaction Energy • Temperature

Theory | The reaction is a chemiluminescence reaction, and like most reactions, its rate is temperature dependent. The lightstick contains dilute hydrogen peroxide in a phthalic ester solvent which is held in a thin glass ampule. This ampule is surrounded by a solution containing phenyl oxalate and a fluorescent dye [9,10-bis(phenylethynyl) anthracene or 9,10-diphenyl anthracene]. When the ampule is broken, the peroxide and the phenyl oxalate ester react. During the course of the reaction, an intermediate is produced which transfers energy to the dye molecule. Visible light is emitted when the excited dye returns to the ground state.

Materials | 400-mL Beakers (2)
Ice
Hot plate or Bunsen burner
Commercial lightsticks (2)

Safety Precautions | Be careful not to puncture the outer plastic tube of the lightstick. According to the manufacturer, the materials in the lightsticks are relatively non hazardous, but common sense dictates that the solutions be kept contained. Wear chemical splash goggles and always follow laboratory safety rules while performing demonstrations.

Demonstration | Fill one of the beakers with hot water (<60 °C), and the other with ice water. Place a lightstick in each beaker, and allow about 3 minutes for temperature equilibration. Following the directions for the lightstick, break the inner ampule of each. The one that was in the hot water will be significantly brighter than the one that was in the ice water.

Lightsticks do have a shelf life! Older materials do not work as well. It seems that they start to lose power after about a year, and after about four years, they will not react at all. Use fresh lightsticks! The light green/yellow lightsticks seem to work better. Hint: pre heat/cool light sticks to save time.

Disposal | Used lightsticks may be discarded in the trash.

Reference | Institute for Chemical Education, University of Wisconsin—Madison, Madison WI.

Marbles and Collision Theory

A down-to-earth activity to demonstrate collision theory.

Application	Collision Theory • Kinetics
Theory	Collision theory explains the rate at which reactions occur. According to the theory the rate of reaction is dependent upon two factors: first, the number of collisions between reactants per unit of time, and second the fraction of these collisions that produce new species. Particles that contain sufficient energy will overcome the repulsive forces of each other's electron clouds and collide effectively. If the collision geometry is just right the collision will result in the formation of a new species.
	This demonstration utilizes magnetic marbles that have the ability to simulate the attractive and repulsive forces involved in chemical interaction. The activity involves rolling marbles toward each other. Those marbles that exhibit the correct collision geometry and magnetic orientation will join, others will be deflected.
Materials	Magnetic marbles available from Flinn Scientific, AP2099.
Safety Precautions	Wear chemical splash goggles and always follow laboratory safety rules while performing demonstrations.
Demonstration	This demonstration requires active participation from a group of students. Perhaps you may wish to use this as an activity for the entire class.
	With a soft leaded pencil, lightly draw a circle, one meter in diameter, on the floor. Have six students sit around this circle, facing inward. Give each student one or two magnetic marbles and instruct them to role their marbles from behind the circle towards the marble of another student in the group. As students continue rolling their marbles, they will find that at times two marbles will collide and form a pair, while others will be deflected. Relate this attraction and repulsion to the collisions that occur between atoms.
Disposal	None required.
Reference	Anne Mundy, "Marbles, Magnetism and Matter" in *The Science Teacher,* May 1989, p 25.

William Tell and the Iodine Clock Reaction

Ten iodine clock reactions are sequenced to the William Tell Overture. Demonstrate the dependence of reaction rates on concentration,

Application

Kinetics • Oscillating Reaction • Redox

Theory

The reaction takes place in three steps:

1. $3 H_2SO_3 + HIO_3 \rightarrow 3 H_2SO_4 + HI$ *fast reaction*
2. $5 HI + HIO_3 \rightarrow 3H_2O + 3I_2$ (blue complex)
3. $H_2SO_3 + H_2O + I_2 \rightarrow H_2SO_4 + 2HI$ (clear) *instantaneous!*

Reaction 3 is instantaneous, reducing iodine to iodide ion as soon as the iodine forms in reaction 2. When the hydrogen sulfite ion (from H_2SO_3) is used up, iodine can no longer be reduced, and it then reacts with the starch to produce the blue complex.

Materials

Water, distilled or de-ionized
Sulfuric acid, 6 M, H_2SO_4
Potassium iodate, KIO_3
Sodium bisulfite, $NaHSO_3$
Soluble starch
Clear plastic cups (20)
Plastic cocktail stirrers (10)
Music from William Tell Overture

Safety Precautions

Sulfuric acid is severely corrosive to eyes, skin and other tissue; considerable heat of dilution with water; even very dilute solutions are harmful to eyes and skin. Sodium bisulfite is a severe irritant to skin and tissue as an aqueous solution. Potassium iodate is an oxidizer and a tissue irritant. Wear chemical splash goggles, chemical-resistant gloves and a chemical-resistant apron.

Preparation

Prepare solutions A and B and then 10 sets of dilutions.

Solution A: 2.0 g KIO_3 per liter of water.

Solution B: 2.0 g soluble starch in 500 mL water, bring to a boil, cool, add 0.40 g $NaHSO_3$ and 5.0 mL 6 M H_2SO_4. Dilute to 1 L with water. Starch solution can also be prepared by adding 30 mL liquid laundry starch to 500 mL water.

Divide the solutions using the following ratios (mL):

Solution A Dilution:

Cup #	A1	A2	A3	A4	A5	A6	A7	A8	A9	A10
Soln A	50	48	45	42	39	36	34	32	29	27
Water	0	2	5	8	11	14	16	18	21	23

Solution B Dilution:

Cup #	B1	B2	B3	B4	B5	B6	B7	B8	B9	B10
Soln B	50	48	45	42	39	36	34	32	29	27
Water	0	2	5	8	11	14	16	18	21	23

A pre-recorded tape is made of three portions of the William Tell Overture: 1) the horn call that introduces the last section of the overture (use about 14 sec); 2) about 29 sec. of the "galloping theme" as it is repeated for the last time, and 3) the coda or ending (the last 23 sec.) This gives a total playing time of a little over 1 min.

Demonstration

Ten volunteers are needed. Each volunteer is asked to hold one pair of solutions (A & B). The music is started and the "conductor" gives the cue at the end of the horn call to pour A into B and mix. It is expected that solution pair ten will change as the music comes to an end.

Note: This demo requires practice! Temperature has a drastic effect on the rate of reaction. Use fresh solutions only. Test with full strength A and B just prior to doing the dilutions. Equal volumes of undiluted A and B should react in about ten seconds. If too fast, dilute solution A slightly with water. If too slow, add a few more drops of sulfuric acid to solution B. Make sure that your volunteers understand that they are not to mix until given the cue. Have them stir continuously. Ham it up as the "conductor"!

Disposal

Solutions can be flushed down the drain with excess water.

Reference

Brice, L. K. *J. Chem. Ed.,* **1980,** *57,* 152.

Reaction Rates and The 1812 Overture

Twelve iodine clock reactions are sequenced to The 1812 Overture to demonstrate the dependence of reaction rates on concentration.

Application | Kinetics • Oscillation • Reaction • Redox

Theory | The reaction takes place in three steps:

1. $3 H_2SO_3 + HIO_3 \rightarrow 3 H_2SO_4 + HI$ *fast reaction*
2. $5 HI + HIO_3 \rightarrow 3H_2O + 3I_2$ (blue complex)
3. $H_2SO_3 + H_2O + I_2 \rightarrow H_2SO_4 + 2HI$ (clear) *instantaneous!*

Reaction 3 is instantaneous, reducing iodine to iodide ion as soon as the iodine forms in reaction 2. When the hydrogen sulfite ion (from H_2SO_3) is used up, iodine can no longer be reduced, and it then reacts with the starch to produce the blue complex.

Materials | 125-mL Flasks, (12)
120 × 150 mm Test tubes (12)
Sulfuric acid, conc., H_2SO_4
Potassium iodate, KIO_3
Sodium bisulfite, $NaHSO_3$
Starch solution, 250 mL
Edited tape of Tchaikovsky's 1812 Overture

Safety Precautions | Sulfuric acid is severely corrosive to eyes, skin and other tissue; considerable heat of dilution with water; even very dilute solutions are harmful to eyes and skin. Sodium bisulfite is a severe irritant to skin and tissue as an aqueous solution. Potassium iodate is an oxidizer and a tissue irritant. Wear chemical splash goggles, chemical-resistant gloves and a chemical-resistant apron.

Preparation | Prepare solutions:

0.1 M H_2SO_3: add 5.2 g $NaHSO_3$ and 1.4 mL concentrated H_2SO_4 to distilled water make 500 mL of solution.

0.1 M HIO_3 add 10.7 g KIO_3 and 1.4 mL concentrated H_2SO_4 to distilled water to make 1 liter of solution.

Starch solution: dissolve 10 g soluble starch to 250 mL hot water or use 25 mL of liquid laundry starch in 250 mL of distilled water.

Note: Solutions are best if freshly mixed. Practice! This is a lot of work, but if you can pull it off, your students will remember it forever! If it doesn't work, you can generate a lot of discussion as to why it didn't. Be sure to make an effort to have students understand the concept of a limiting reagent and the rate determining step before you try this.

These directions were prepared for a room at 20 to 22 °C. Constant room temperature, a critical factor, must be maintained.

Demonstration

The familiar iodine clock reaction is performed in 12 different reaction vessels. The amount of the limiting reagent is different in each reaction mixture. The appearance of the blue color is timed to the cannon blasts of Tchaikovsky's 1812 Overture.

Each of twelve assistants is given a numbered flask containing 5 mL of H_2SO_3 solution, 5 mL of the starch solution, and 100 mL of water. In addition, they are given a corresponding numbered test tube containing a different volume of the 0.1 M HIO_3. The volumes and expected time of reaction for these test tubes are as follows:

Test tube	0.1M HIO_3	ETA of Blue
1	11.0 mL	13 sec
2	10.0 mL	15 sec
3	9.3 mL	18 sec
4	8.1 mL	21 sec
5	7.7 mL	23 sec
6	7.5 mL	25 sec
7	7.3 mL	26 sec
8	7.2 mL	28 sec
9	6.7 mL	31 sec
10	5.8 mL	35 sec
11	5.4 mL	38 sec
12	4.0 mL	70 sec

Each assistant is told to await the instructor's hand signal. They are directed that when the hand signal is given, they are to mix, in unison, the contents of their test tube into their flask, swirl the flask, and return the flask to the demonstration table, keeping the flasks in correct numerical order. The hand signal is given at the correct time (3 minutes and 42 seconds into this version of the tape). Then we all stand back and pray.

Disposal

Solutions can be flushed down the drain with excess water.

Reference

Whitman, M. *J. Chem. Ed.,* **1983,** *60,* 229.

Draw Poker — It's All Entropy!

The odds of dealing a Royal Flush are used to illustrate the concept of entropy.

Application Entropy • Spontaneous Reactions • Disorder

Theory The probability that a poker hand will contain five specific cards is the same, regardless of which five cards are specified. Thus there is an equal probability of dealing 10♥ J♥ Q♥ K♥ A♥ as dealing a hand containing 2♣ 4♥ 10♥ 8♣ J♦. However the first hand, a royal flush, strikes us as more highly ordered than the second hand, a "nothing" hand. The reason for this is clear. There are only 4 poker hands that are in the "state" of a royal flush; in contrast there are over 1.3 million nothing hands. The nothing state has a higher degree of disorder than the royal flush state because there are so many more arrangements of cards that correspond to the nothing state.

We can use the same reasoning for chemical systems. For example, consider two states for the gas molecules:

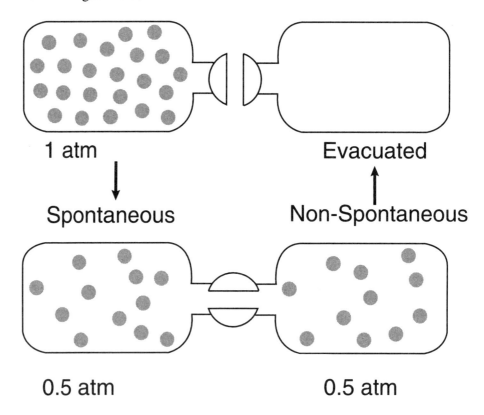

1 atm → Spontaneous

Evacuated ← Non-Spontaneous

0.5 atm   0.5 atm

When the stopcock is opened the volume available to the atoms is doubled. There are more possible arrangements of the atoms in the second figure than in the first; thus the randomness of the latter is greater than the former.

Materials	A deck of cards.
Safety Precautions	Always follow laboratory safety rules while performing demonstrations.
Demonstration	Deal two hands—face up:

$\qquad$ 10-♠, Jack-♠, Queen-♠, King-♠, Ace-♠

$\qquad$ 5 random cards

Discuss the odds of obtaining a royal flush in terms of entropy. Repeat several times dealing two or more hands.

Catalytic Oxidation of Acetone

The oxidation of acetone is catalyzed by copper.

Application | Catalysts • Oxidation • Organic Chemistry

Theory | Ketones, such as acetone (propanone) may be oxidized along the surface of copper to yield acids, such as formic and acetic acids. The copper must be heated to red-hot for the catalytic reaction to take place. The oxidation of acetone is highly exothermic and the heat evolved will continue to drive the reaction.

Materials | Acetone
125-mL Erlenmeyer flask
U.S. penny (1982 or earlier)
Copper wire
Bunsen burner

Safety Precautions | Acetone is flammable, a dangerous fire risk, and toxic by ingestion and inhalation. Formic and acetic acid fumes are toxic by inhalation, very flammable and a dangerous fire and explosion risk. This demonstration is best done in a fume hood. Do not use the Bunsen burner near the acetone and turn off immediately after heating the penny. Wear chemical splash goggles, chemical-resistant gloves and a chemical-resistant apron. Have a fire extinguisher available.

Preparation | Drill a small hole into a penny (1982 or earlier). Attach a heavy copper wire (approx. 18 ga.) through this hole.

Demonstration | Pour 10 mL acetone into a 125-mL Erlenmeyer flask. Drill a small hole into a penny (1982 or earlier). Attach a heavy copper wire (approx. 18 ga.) through this hole. Heat the penny in a Bunsen burner until red hot, then quickly suspend the hot penny just above but not touching the surface of the acetone. The penny will continue to glow until the acetone is consumed.

Hint: Bend the copper wire so it can hang over the lip of the flask and still suspend the hot penny just above the acetone.

Disposal | Evaporate the remaining acetone in a hood.

Chapter 15

Equilibrium

Common Ion Effect II

Demonstrate the effect of acetate ion on the acidity of acetic acid.

Application | Acids and Bases • Equilibrium • Reaction Rates • pH • Buffers

Theory | The reaction rate between calcium carbonate and acid is mainly dependent on the hydrogen ion concentration in the acid. 2 M hydrochloric acid, 2 M acetic acid, and 2 M acetic acid with an additional 2 M acetate ion concentration react at correspondingly slower rates. The foam produced is the result of CO_2 gas production. The reaction is:

$$CaCO_3(s) + 2\,H^+(aq) \rightarrow CO_2(g) + H_2O(l) + Ca^{2+}(aq)$$

The rate at which the foam rises is dependent on the rate of CO_2 production. The concentration of H^+ ion in the 2 M HCl is highest, lower in the 2 M acetic acid because of incomplete ionization in a weak acid, and lower still in the acetic acid with acetate ion mixture due to shifting of the ionization equilibrium. This is the so-called common ion effect. The equation is:

$$HC_2H_3O_2 \rightleftharpoons H^+ + C_2H_3O_2^- \qquad\qquad K_a = 1.8 \times 10^{-5}$$

The $[H^+]$ in 2 M acetic acid is 0.006 M. When acetate ions are added, the equilibrium is shifted to the left, toward the undissociated acid. The result is a decrease in $[H^+]$ to about 0.00002 M.

Materials | Universal indicator (2 mL)
Calcium carbonate, $CaCO_3$ (75 g)
Acetic acid, 2M, $HC_2H_3O_2$ (180 mL)
Sodium acetate, $NaC_2H_3O_2 \cdot 3H_2O$ (27 g)
Distilled or deionized water (20 mL)
Hydrochloric acid, 2 M, HCl (100 mL)
Pipet
250-mL Glass cylinders (3)
100-mL Graduated cylinders (3)

Safety Precautions | Hydrochloric acid is highly toxic by ingestion or inhalation; severely corrosive to skin and eyes. Acetic acid is corrosive to skin and tissue, a moderate fire risk, and toxic by ingestion. Sodium acetate is a skin, eye and respiratory irritant. Wear chemical splash goggles, chemical-resistant gloves and a chemical-resistant apron.

Preparation | Prepare the 2 M acid solutions. To 80 mL of the 2 M acetic acid solution, add the sodium acetate, dissolve, and dilute to a volume of 100 mL with distilled water in one of the 100-mL graduates. Measure out 100 mL of the HCl solution in another graduated cylinder and 100-mL of the 2 M acetic acid in a third. Place 10 drops of the universal indicator in the bottom of each of the three 250-mL cylinders and cover the bottom of each with 25 grams of the calcium carbonate powder.

Demonstration With the aid of an assistant, simultaneously pour the contents of the three graduated cylinders into the three 250-mL cylinders. Frothing will occur in all three, but it will be nearly instantaneous in the cylinder with HCl, somewhat slower in the cylinder with acetic acid, and significantly slower in the acetic acid–acetate ion cylinder. In addition, the universal indicator will show differences in the acidity (pH) of the mixtures.

Disposal The solution can be flushed down the drain with excess water.

References Shakhashiri, B. Z. *Chemical Demonstrations;* University of Wisconsin: Madison, WI, 1989; Vol. III; p 155.

Sorum, C. H. *J. Chem. Ed.* **1948,** *25,* 489.

Kinetics of a Blue Bottle

A kinetic study of the classic *Disappearing Blue* clock reaction.

Application | Kinetics • Reaction Rates • Solutions • Redox

Theory | The reaction involves the reduction of methylene blue by an alkaline glucose (dextrose) solution. Upon shaking, the reduced product (colorless) is reoxidized to the blue dye by dissolved oxygen. The reaction proceeds in 4 steps, essentially the following:

$$O_2(g) \rightarrow O_2(aq)$$

$$\text{Methylene blue} + O_2 \rightarrow \text{Methylene blue}$$
$$\text{(colorless)} \qquad\qquad \text{(blue)}$$

$$\text{Glucose} + OH^- \rightarrow \text{Glucoside}$$

$$\text{Glucoside} + \text{Methylene blue} \rightarrow \text{Methylene blue} + OH^-(aq) + \text{glucose}$$
$$\text{(blue)} \qquad\qquad \text{(colorless)}$$

Materials | 250-mL Erlenmeyer flasks (8) solid rubber stoppers (8)
600-mL beakers for water baths (4)
Potassium hydroxide, KOH
Glucose
Methylene Blue, 1% solution
Hot plates (2)
Ice
100-mL Graduated cylinder

Safety Precautions | Potassium hydroxide is corrosive to skin and eyes. Methylene blue is moderately toxic by ingestion. Wear chemical splash goggles, chemical-resistant gloves and a chemical-resistant apron.

Preparation | Prepare the blue bottle solution by dissolving 27 g potassium hydroxide, KOH, in 1000 mL distilled or deionized water, cool and add 33 g of dextrose, swirl to dissolve, and then add a few drops of 1% methylene blue solution. It works best if fresh. It does not keep very well. Prepare 4 water baths at the following temperatures: 10 °C, 20 °C, 30 °C, and 40 °C.

Demonstration | **Temperature Effect:** Put 100 mL of the solution into each of four 250-mL Erlenmeyer flasks and stopper tightly. Place a flask in each water bath and let stand for 5 minutes. As you remove a flask from the water bath, start timing and shake the flask five times. Return the flask to the bath and continue timing until the color fades. Repeat for the other flasks.

Concentration Effect: Put 100 mL of solution into 4 more flasks. Add pellets of solid KOH as follows: 2 pellets to the first flask, 4 pellets to the second, 6 to the third and 8 to the fourth. Stopper, swirl to dissolve, and let stand until all are colorless. Shake the first flask five times again, and start timing until the color fades. Repeat with each flask in turn.

Disposal

Neutralize the solution before disposal according to Flinn Suggested Disposal Method #10.

Reference

Summerlin, L. R.; and Ealy, J. L. *Chemical Demonstrations,* 2nd ed.; American Chemical Society: Washington, DC, 1988; Vol. 1, p 127.

Equilibrium Between N_2O_4 and NO_2

Demonstrate the effect of temperature on the equilibrium of two gases.

Application | Equilibrium • Le Chatlier's Principle • Gases

Theory | Nitrogen dioxide, NO_2, a dark brown gas, and dinitrogen tetraoxide, N_2O_4, a colorless gas, exist in equilibrium with each other:

$$2\,NO_2(g) \rightleftharpoons N_2O_4(g)$$
$$\text{Brown} \qquad \text{Colorless}$$

At room temperature and above, the mixture is normally brown in color, indicating a higher concentration of nitrogen dioxide. Upon cooling, the forward reaction is favored which in turn increases the concentration of the dinitrogen tetraoxide, resulting in a yellowish colored gas mixture. In fact, the yellow color is due to traces of nitrogen dioxide (brown) mixed with the colorless dinitrogen tetraoxide. If the mixture is cooled sufficiently the nitrogen dioxide gas concentration can be significantly reduced. Salt is added to the ice to lower its temperature.

Materials | Nitrogen dioxide diffusion tube available from Flinn (AP8476)
    or
Nitrogen dioxide gas cylinder, or generator (see advanced preparation)
250-mL Florence flasks (3) with rubber stoppers (3)
1000-mL beakers, or shallow pans (2)
Ice and salt water mixture
Hot water or hot plate

Safety Precautions | Nitrogen dioxide and dinitrogen tetraoxide are both toxic by inhalation and poisonous. This demo must be done only under a fume hood. Nitrogen dioxide is corrosive to rubber stoppers: do not store the filled flasks longer than a day. Wear chemical splash goggles, chemical-resistant gloves and a chemical-resistant apron.

Preparation | Nitrogen dioxide gas may be produced by reacting copper turnings with concentrated nitric acid in a gas generating apparatus. Immerse a Florence flask into a 1000-mL beaker filled with ice and salt. Slowly introduce nitrogen dioxide gas into the flask by upward displacement of air. The brown-colored gas will be visible. Stopper the flask tightly. Repeat with the other two flasks. Store in a cool area.

Demonstration | Place one flask into a 1000-mL beaker half-filled with hot water. Allow this flask to warm a few minutes. Meanwhile place a second flask into a beaker containing ice mixed with salt. Allow this flask to cool. The third flask may serve as a control for the experiment.

Disposal | Flush flasks with water in a fume hood to dissolve the nitrogen dioxide gas then dispose by flushing down a drain with excess water.

Reference | Wilbraham, A. *Chemistry;* Addison Wesley: Menlo Park, CA, 1987; p 418.

Nitrogen Gas Evolution Oscillator

A unique oscillating reaction producing gas bubbles.

Application | Oscillating Reactions • Gases • Redox

Theory | Nitrogen gas is produced in an aqueous reaction and slowly forms into ever increasingly large bubbles until they are large enough to rise to the surface. Note that some NO_2 appears at the surface, probably due to the side reaction of aqueous HNO_2 forming NO which then reacts with O_2 above the surface.

$$NH_4^+(aq) + NO_2^-(aq) \rightarrow N_2(aq) + 2H_2O$$

$$N_2(aq) \rightleftarrows N_2(g)$$

The concentration of dissolved nitrogen, which is changing due to formation of nitrogen gas bubbles, controls the oscillating reaction.

Materials | Ammonium sulfate, $(NH_4)SO_4$ (26 g)
Sulfuric acid, 0.2 M, H_2SO_4 (100 mL)
Sodium nitrite, $NaNO_2$ (28 g)
Distilled water (100 mL)
250-mL Flasks (2)
Stoppers (2)
100-mL Beaker or large test tube (25 × 200 nm)

Safety Precautions | Sulfuric acid is severely corrosive to eyes, skin and other tissue; considerable heat of dilution with water; even very dilute solutions are harmful to eyes and skin. Sodium nitrite is a strong oxidizer, toxic and a fire and explosion risk if heated. Wear chemical splash goggles, chemical-resistant gloves and a chemical-resistant apron.

Preparation | Dissolve the ammonium sulfate in the sulfuric acid. Dissolve the sodium nitrite in the distilled water.

Demonstration | Pour 10 mL of each solution into a 100-mL beaker and stir rapidly for 5 seconds. Effervescence will appear, then subside, then redevelop with intermissions of about 8 to 10 seconds continuing for about 3 to 4 minutes.

Note: This also works on an Alyea projector on the overhead if you have one. Use a test tube and 3 mL of each solution. Mix by shaking a few times.

Disposal | Solution can be flushed down the drain with excess water.

Reference | Shakashiri, B. Z. *Chemical Demonstrations;* University of Wisconsin: Madison, WI, 1985; Vol. 2, pp 301–304.

Equilibrium on an Overhead

Demonstrate a chemical equilibrium system on the overhead projector.

Application | Reaction Rates • Equilibrium

Theory | The demonstration is based on the following equilibrium:

$$CuSO_4 + 4KBr \rightleftarrows K_2[CuBr_4] + K_2SO_4$$
$$\text{blue} \quad \text{colorless} \quad\quad \text{green} \quad \text{colorless}$$

Materials | 100-mL Beakers, (3)
400-mL Beakers, (3)
Stirring rods (3)
250-mL Graduated cylinder
50-mL Graduated cylinders, (3)
Overhead projector
Hot plate or Bunsen burner/ring stand
Ice bath
Cupric sulfate, 0.17 M, $CuSO_4$
Potassium bromide, sat. solution, KBr
Sodium sulfate, sat. solution, Na_2SO_4

Safety Precautions | Copper sulfate is toxic by ingestion and inhalation and is a skin and respiratory irritant. Potassium bromide is potentially toxic by ingestion. Wear chemical splash goggles, chemical-resistant gloves and a chemical-resistant apron.

Preparation | Make up the following solutions: 0.17 M cupric sulfate: 24.5 g $CuSO_4 \cdot 5H_2O$ in 500 mL H_2O. Saturated solution of potassium bromide: 53 g KBr in 100 mL H_2O. Saturated solution of sodium sulfate: 20 g Na_2SO_4 in 100 mL H_2O. Measure 150 mL of the cupric sulfate solution into each of the three 400-mL beakers. Measure 50 mL of the potassium bromide into each of two 50-mL beakers. Measure 50 mL of the sodium sulfate into the third 50-mL beaker.

Demonstration | Show the cupric sulfate solutions on the overhead or light box. Keep one of the solutions apart to use as a reference.

While stirring, add 50 mL of the KBr solution to two of the $CuSO_4$ solutions. The color changes from blue to green, showing the formation of $K_2[CuBr_4]$. Add 50 mL H_2O to the reference beaker to account for dilution.

While stirring, add 50 mL of Na_2SO_4 solution to one of the green solutions. The color changes back to blue, showing that the equilibrium has been shifted to the left. Again add 50 mL of H_2O to each of the other beakers to account for dilution.

Remove the blue solution prepared in step 3 from the overhead and heat. As it gets hot, the color becomes green again, showing that the equilibrium has been shifted to the right. Caution! Do not place the hot beaker directly on the overhead stage, instead, hold the beaker about 2 cm above the stage.

Finally, place the heated solution into the ice bath to cool. Show that the color changes back to blue, showing an equilibrium shift again.

Disposal Solutions can be flushed down the drain with excess water.

Reference Burke, B. A. *J. Chem. Ed.* **1977,** *54,* 29.

An Oscillating Clock Reaction

A simple yellow–blue–yellow oscillating reaction.

Application Kinetics • Redox

Theory The mechanism is not completely understood, however, it is similar in some respects to the iodine clock reaction. There are a series of complex reactions that occur. In the first series, oxygen gas and iodine are formed. The iodine reacts with the starch to form the typical blue complex. As the iodine is used up in another series of reactions, the complex is broken down and the color fades, but is formed again when the concentration of iodine increases again. Each reaction is reversible, and rates are concentration dependent, so the system goes through a large number of oscillations before one or more of the reactants are used up.

Materials 500-mL Beaker
Magnetic stirrer
Hydrogen peroxide, 30% solution, H_2O_2 (40 mL)
Potassium Iodate, KIO_3, (4.3 g)
Sulfuric acid, conc., H_2SO_4 (0.5 mL)
Soluble starch or liquid laundry starch
Malonic acid (7.8 g)
Manganese Sulfate, $MnSO_4 \cdot H_2O$ (1.7 g)

Safety Precautions Hydrogen peroxide is severely corrosive to the skin, eyes, and respiratory tract; a very strong oxidant; and a dangerous fire and explosion risk. Sulfuric acid is severely corrosive to eyes, skin and other tissue; considerable heat of dilution with water; even very dilute solutions are harmful to eyes and skin. Potassium iodate is an oxidizer and tissue irritant. Manganese sulfate may be a tissue irritant. Malonic acid is a strong irritant, moderately toxic and, when dissolved in water, a strong acid that is corrosive to eyes, skin and respiratory tract. Malonic acid is regulated in some states, please check local regulations before purchasing. Wear chemical splash goggles, chemical-resistant gloves and a chemical-resistant apron.

Preparation Prepare solutions A, B, and C as described.

Solution A: Add 40 mL of 30% hydrogen peroxide to 100 mL of water.

Solution B: While stirring, add 4.3 g of KIO_3 and 0.5 mL of concentrated sulfuric acid to 100 mL of water.

Solution C: Prepare a paste of 0.15 g of soluble starch in hot water or add 15 mL of liquid laundry starch. While stirring, add this to 500 mL of hot water. Then add 7.8 g of malonic acid and 1.7 g of $MnSO_4 \cdot H_2O$.

Demonstration Place 100 mL of solution A in a 500-mL beaker on a magnetic stirrer. Set the stirrer on a low setting. Add 100 mL of solution B. Then add 100 mL of solution C. The color of the solution will begin to oscillate from light yellow to blue to light yellow in a few seconds. The oscillations are accompanied by the evolution of CO_2 and O_2 gas.

Disposal All solutions may be flushed down the drain with excess water.

Reference Summerlin, L., et al. *Chemical Demonstrations;* American Chemical Society: Washington, DC, 1986; Vol. 1, p 113.

Ostwald Oxidation of Ammonia

Ammonia is oxidized to a nitrate using a platinum catalyst.

Application | Catalysis • Equilibrium • Thermochemistry • Industrial Chemistry

Theory | The Haber process is an important industrial process that produces ammonia from hydrogen and nitrogen. The Ostwald oxidation converts ammonia first to the oxide, then to nitrates. Nitrates are important to the fertilizer and explosives industries.

$$4NH_3 + 5O_2 \rightarrow 4NO + 6H_2O + 215 \text{ kcal}$$

$$2NO + O_2 \rightarrow 2NO_2 + 27.8 \text{ kcal}$$

$$3NO_2 + H_2O \rightarrow 2HNO_3 + NO \text{ (recycled)}$$

Materials | 500-mL Filter flask
Platinum wire (20 cm)
Ammonia, conc. solution, NH_4OH
Bunsen burner
Glass tube
Oxygen source–optional

Safety Precautions | Ammonia is toxic by inhalation and ingestion; both liquid and vapor are extremely irritating, especially to the eyes. Perform only in a well ventilated area or in a fume hood. This reaction gets very hot! Occasional explosions can occur if mixture is enriched with pure oxygen. Wear chemical splash goggles, chemical-resistant gloves and a chemical-resistant apron.

Preparation | None required.

Demonstration | Using a filter flask provides a built-in 'handle'. Coil the platinum wire, pre-heat it to glowing and hang it in the flask by hooking it over the mouth of the flask containing about 100 mL of concentrated (12 M) ammonia solution.

The wire will glow red hot due to the reaction. Blowing into the flask from a glass tube enriches or restores some of the oxygen content. Adding pure oxygen by slowly bubbling into the ammonia, causes significant increases in reactions. Careful, however, since this might cause small explosions. This is very effective if you can do it in a darkened room.

Disposal | Flush solutions down the drain after neutralizing, using Flinn Suggested Disposal Method #10.

Copper Chloride Equilibrium

Demonstrate the effect of concentration on an equilibrium reaction.

Application | Equilibrium • Le Chatelier's Principle

Theory | A solution of cupric chloride in ethanol is green due to the presence of copper chloride containing species such as $CuCl_2(H_2O)_2$. Addition of water turns the solution blue as water molecules replace the chloride ions in the coordination sphere around the copper. The reaction is:

$$CuCl_2(H_2O)_2 + 2\,H_2O \rightarrow Cu(H_2O)_4^{2+} + 2Cl^-$$
$$\text{(green)} \qquad\qquad\qquad \text{(blue)}$$

As predicted by LeChatelier's principle, the reaction is shifted back towards reactants by the addition of excess chloride ion in the HCl.

Materials | Cupric chloride dihydrate, $CuCl_2 \cdot 2H_2O$
Hydrochloric acid, conc., HCl
Ethanol, C_2H_5OH
Distilled or deionized water
125-mL Erlenmeyer flasks (2)

Safety Precuations | Hydrochloric acid is a severe skin and respiratory irritant, highly toxic by ingestion or inhalation, and severely corrosive to eyes and skin. Cupric chloride is toxic by ingestion. Ethanol is a dangerous fire risk, flammable and the addition of denaturant makes the product poisonous. Wear chemical splash goggles, chemical-resistant gloves and a chemical-resistant apron.

Preparation | Prepare 200 mL of a 0.1 M $CuCl_2 \cdot 2H_2O$ solution in ethanol.

Demonstration | Note the green color of the solution. Add sufficient distilled or deionized water to shift the color to blue. Divide this solution equally between the two flasks. To one of the flasks add sufficient conc. HCl to restore the green color.

Disposal | All solutions can be flushed down the drain with excess water.

Reference | Diemente, D. *J. Chem. Ed.* **1991,** *68,* 568.

Chapter 16

Redox

Oxidation of Glycerin

Demonstrate a spontaneous redox reaction.

Application Kinetics • Activation Energy • Redox

Theory The reaction between glycerin and potassium permanganate is highly exothermic. It does not start immediately, but will begin in 15 to 20 seconds. You can tell when the reaction is about to begin because a slight puff of smoke forms in the center of the pile. The equation for the reaction is:

$$14\ KMnO_4(s) + 4\ C_3H_5(OH)_3(l) \rightarrow$$
$$7\ K_2CO_3(s) + 7\ Mn_2O_3(s) + 5\ CO_2(g) + 16\ H_2O(l)$$

Materials Potassium permanganate, $KMnO_4$ (10 g)
Glycerin (1 mL)
Evaporating dish, porcelain
Dropper

Safety Precautions Potassium permanganate is a very strong oxidizing agent and can explode on sudden heating; a common cause of eye accidents. It is also a strong skin irritant. The reaction produces a flame and intense heat—stand back. Some people are allergic to glycerin and may experience skin and/or eye irritation. This reaction should be done in a fume hood. Wear chemical splash goggles, chemical-resistant gloves and a chemical-resistant apron.

Preparation None required.

Demonstration Place 10 g of the solid potassium permanganate in a pile in the evaporating dish. Add 10 drops of glycerin on top of the pile, enough to just wet the pile. Stand back and observe. A puff of smoke will signal the start, then intense violet flames will be produced.

Disposal Dissolve the solid residue in water, and filter. Dispose of the filtrate by flushing down the drain with excess water, and dispose of the precipitate in the trash.

Reference Summerlin, L. R.; Ealy, J. L. *Chemical Demonstrations;* American Chemical Society: Washington, DC, 1988; Vol. 1, p 122.

Simple Dry Cell Electrolysis

Demonstrate electrolysis of aqueous solutions in a simple, easily visible manner.

Application | Electrolysis • Conductivity • Redox • Decomposition Reactions

Theory | Soluble ionic solids are completely dissociated in aqueous solution, thus their solutions are strong electrolytes. If an electrical current is passed through a solution, The cation is reduced at the cathode (negative electrode), and the anion is oxidized at the anode (positive electrode).

For example, the electrolysis reactions for sodium chloride solution are:

$$\text{Cathode reaction:} \quad Na^+(aq) + e^- \rightarrow Na^0(s)$$

$$\text{Anode reaction:} \quad 2Cl^-(aq) \rightarrow Cl_2(g) + 2e^-$$

Materials | 9 V Battery
Petri dish or 250-mL beaker
Aqueous solutions of NaCl, NaBr, KI, CuCl$_2$
Overhead projector
Phenolphthalein indicator
Starch solution

Safety Precautions | Sodium bromide and cupric chloride are toxic by ingestion or inhalation. Bromine or chlorine gas will be produced which are severe irritants and toxic by inhalation. Use micro quantities or use a fume hood. Wear chemical splash goggles and always follow laboratory safety rules while performing demonstrations.

Preparation | Solutions can be made by dissolving a few grams of the solid in about 100 mL of distilled or deionized water. The concentrations are not critical.

Demonstration | Place the Petri dish on the projector stage, put the battery on its side in the dish, focus, and add the solution until the battery terminals are just covered with solution. Students will be able to observe the evolution of gas bubbles from one or both electrodes. With sodium or potassium salts, a drop or two of phenolphthalein will produce a pink color in the region of the negative terminal (cathode) due to the reaction of the alkali metal with water to form hydroxide ion. With iodides, a drop of starch solution will produce a blue-black color at the positive terminal (anode), due to the formation of the starch–iodine complex. With copper salts, the cathode will acquire a coating of reddish-brown metallic copper.

Disposal | All solutions can be flushed down the drain with excess water.

References | Talesnick, I. *Idea Bank Collation;* S 17 Science Supplies and Services: Kingston, Ontario; 1984; Idea #548.

The Science Teacher **1983,** 50 *(5),* 76.

The Hungry Dragon

Flames and smoke shoot out when wooden splints or Gummy Bears are thrust into a large test tube.

Application

Combustion • Oxidation • Oxidizing Agents • Organic Chemistry • Exothermic Reactions

Theory

Oxygen released from potassium chlorate causes rapid oxidation of organic materials releasing intense heat, light and large amounts of combustion products:

$$2 \, KClO_3(s) \rightarrow 2 \, KCl(s) + 3O_2(g)$$

$$C_XH_YO_Z(s) + O_2(g) \rightarrow CO_2(g) + H_2O(g) + energy$$

Materials

Large Pyrex® test tube (25×250 mm)
Potassium chlorate, $KClO_3$ (5 g)
Ring stand
Utility clamp, without rubber sleeves
Burner
Wooden splints
Candies, small (e.g., M&M's®, Gummy Bears,® etc.)
Tongs or forceps
Table top protection (see safety precautions)

Safety Precautions

Potassium chlorate is a strong oxidizer and an irritant. $KClO_3$ is extremely dangerous since, if only slightly contaminated, it will explode when exposed to moderate shock or when heated. Cover table with non-flammable covering such as sheet metal or fiberglass sheeting (sheet rock or wallboard works well). Use a safety shield in front and behind the reaction to protect yourself and the class. Insert flammables with long tongs or forceps. **Keep hands back!** Never stand in front of apparatus or aim it at anyone.

Preparation

Set up ring stand as shown:

Demonstration | Place 5 g potassium chlorate into a test tube as in diagram. Be certain that the test tube is well clamped to stand. Slant tube as indicated.

Heat test tube until contents have melted.

Using tongs or forceps, thrust a wooden splint into the mouth of the test tube. **Step back as flames and smoke are given off!** (Pink glow is due to potassium flame test).

Add additional splints, **one at a time** until the oxygen gas production is exhausted or until you wish to stop.

Pieces of candies or Gummy Bears may be substituted in place of the splints if desired. The dragon eats the candy, expelling smoke and flames.

Disposal | Rinse thoroughly with excess water and flush down the drain.

A Reversible Redox Reaction

Demonstrate catalyst activity and reversibility of chemical reactions.

Application	Equilibrium • Law of Conservation of Mass • Redox
Theory	The system goes through a series of steps. The cupric ion begins as a catalyst, but later becomes a reactant. In the first step, cupric ion catalyzes the decomposition of hydrogen peroxide.

$$2\,H_2O_2 \xrightarrow{Cu^{2+}} 2\,H_2O + O_2$$

The cupric ion is reduced to cuprous ion in forming the precipitate of cuprous oxide, Cu_2O

$$Cu^{2+} + 1e^- \rightarrow Cu^+$$

Hydrogen peroxide is believed to oxidize the tartrate ion to oxalate ion and carbon dioxide in two steps, with oxalate ion as an intermediate.

$$C_4H_4O_6{}^{2-} + 4\,H_2O_2 \rightarrow C_2O_4{}^{2-} + 2\,CO_2 + 6\,H_2O$$
$$2\,H^+ + C_2O_4{}^{2-} + H_2O_2 \rightarrow 2\,CO_2 + 2H_2O$$

The oxalate ion is oxidized by the cupric ion to carbon dioxide, and the cupric ion is reduced to cuprous ion. This portion of the reaction is very similar to the reaction that occurs with Benedict's solution and a reducing sugar. The orange precipitate of cuprous oxide is identical to that formed in a positive Benedict's test.

$$C_2O_4{}^{2-} + 2Cu^{2+} \rightarrow 2\,CO_2 + 2\,Cu^+$$

Further addition of hydrogen peroxide oxidizes the cuprous ion back to cupric, allowing the cycle to begin again.

$$2\,Cu^+ + 2\,H_2O_2 + 2\,H^+ \rightarrow 2H_2O + 2Cu^{2+}$$

Materials	Cupric sulfate, 1 M, SH_2O Potassium sodium tartrate, 1 M, $KNaC_4H_4O_6 \cdot 4H_2O$ Hydrogen peroxide, 3% solution, H_2O_2 1-L Beaker Hot plate/stirrer Thermometer
Safety Precautions	Hydrogen peroxide is severely corrosive to the skin, eyes, and respiratory tract; a very strong oxidant; and a dangerous fire and explosion risk. Cupric sulfate is a skin and respiratory irritant and is toxic by ingestion and inhalation. Wear chemical splash goggles, chemical-resistant gloves and a chemical-resistant apron.
Preparation	Prepare or purchase the solutions.

Demonstration | Place 60 mL of the tartrate solution and 40 mL of the hydrogen peroxide into a 1-L beaker on a hot plate. Stir the mixture and heat to 50 to 60 °C.

Add 1 mL of 1 M cupric sulfate solution. The solution is initially blue but an orange precipitate of cuprous oxide, Cu_2O, eventually forms.

Add another 40 mL of the hydrogen peroxide and the reaction will go through the light clear blue solution to orange precipitate cycle again. Additional 40 mL portions of hydrogen peroxide will repeat the cycle at least 4 times.

Disposal | The solution can be disposed of by flushing down the drain with excess water.

Reference | Sherman, M. C.; Weil, D. *J. Chem. Ed.* **1991,** 1037.

Photochemical Bleaching of Methylene Blue

Demonstrate that light can act as an energy source for a chemical reaction.

Application | Energy • Redox • Light

Theory | The reaction between ferrous ion and methylene blue (MB) is reversible.

$$Fe^{2+} + \text{oxidized MB} \rightleftharpoons Fe^{3+} + \text{reduced MB}$$

(blue)   (colorless)

Materials | Ferrous sulfate, $FeSO_4$
Sulfuric acid, 0.1 M, H_2SO_4
Methylene blue, 1% solution
Overhead projector or other concentrated light source
150-mL Beakers (2)

Safety Precautions | Sulfuric acid is severely corrosive to eyes, skin and other tissue; considerable heat of dilution with water; even very dilute solutions are harmful to eyes and skin. Methylene blue is moderately toxic. Ferrous sulfate is toxic by ingestion. Wear chemical splash goggles, chemical-resistant gloves and a chemical-resistant apron.

Preparation | Dissolve 1 gram of the ferrous sulfate in 50 mL of 0.1 M sulfuric acid. Add enough of the methylene blue solution to produce a definite blue color (3 to 6 drops). Divide the solution into two 150-mL beakers.

Demonstration | Place one of the beakers on an overhead projector and turn on the projector for a few seconds, irradiating the solution with light. The solution will become nearly colorless. Compare to the second beaker. The colorless solution will return to its original blue color after being removed from the light source for a minute or two. The process can be repeated several times.

Disposal | Neutralize the solution with sodium carbonate before flushing down the drain with excess water.

Reference | Kathleen Dombrink, McCluer North High School, Florissant, MO, at Woodrow Wilson Chem 4 Institute.

Autocatalysis of a Redox Reaction

A product from a redox reaction is a catalyst to accelerate the reaction.

Application | Redox • Catalysis

Theory | The reaction between permanganate and oxalate ions is relatively slow at normal temperatures but is accelerated when manganous ions are added to the reaction mixture. Since the manganous ion is one of the products, its ability to catalyze the reaction is called autocatalysis. The reaction is:

$$2\ MnO_4^- + 5\ C_2O_4^{2-} + 16\ H^+ \xrightarrow{Mn^{2+}} 10\ CO_2 + 2\ Mn^{2+} + 8\ H_2O$$

Materials | Sulfuric acid, conc., H_2SO_4
Potassium permanganate, 0.01 M, $KMnO_4$ (200 mL)
Sodium oxalate, 0.05 M, $Na_2C_2O_4$
Manganese sulfate, 0.1 M, $MnSO_4 \cdot 7\ H_2O$
100-mL Graduate cylinders (2)
100-mL Beakers (2)

Note: Winkler's reagent or $MnCl_2$ may be used as an alternate source of the Mn^{2+} ion.

Safety Precautions | Sulfuric acid is severely corrosive to eyes, skin and other tissue; considerable heat of dilution with water; even very dilute solutions are harmful to eyes and skin. Potassium permanganate is a powerful oxidizing agent, can explode on sudden heating, common cause of eye injuries; also a strong skin irritant. Wear chemical splash goggles, chemical-resistant gloves and a chemical-resistant apron.

Preparation | Prepare solutions: 0.01 M $KMnO_4$ 0.32 g in 200 mL, 0.05 M $Na_2C_2O_4$ is 1.4 g in 200 mL solution and 0.1 M $MnSO_4 \cdot 7\ H_2O$ is 1.7 g in 100 mL.

Demonstration | Prepare two cylinders with 50 mL each of 0.01 M potassium permanganate. Acidify 100 mL of 0.05 M sodium oxalate with 10 drops of concentrated sulfuric acid, stir and separate equally into two beakers. Add 3 drops of 0.1 M $MnSO_4$ to one of the beakers containing sodium oxalate. Now pour the solutions from the beakers into the cylinders with potassium permanganate (one in each cylinder). Note the times needed for each reaction to occur.

Disposal | All solutions may be flushed down a sink with excess water.

Reference | Summerlin, L. R.; Ealy, J. L. Chemical Demonstrations; American Chemical Society: Washington, DC, 1988; Vol. 2, p 156.

Silver Plate — Magic Mirror

Mirrors are traditionally made by plating pure silver metal on one side of a piece of glass. Silvering is also applied to the insides of such items as glass lamp bases.

Application Redox • Qualitative Analysis • Metals • Stoichiometry • Applied Chemistry

Theory Silver nitrate contains silver ions which are complexed and kept soluble in the presence of ammonium ions from ammonium nitrate. The silver ions are then precipitated by sodium hydroxide in the form of silver oxide/hydroxide. The mixture is then reduced, slowly, by sucrose and tartaric acid leaving a silver layer, only atoms thick, on the interior surface of a glass container.

$$Ag^{+1} + 2NH_3 \rightarrow Ag(NH_3)_2{}^{+1}$$

$$Ag(NH_3)_2{}^{+1} + OH^{-1} \rightarrow AgOH/Ag_2O$$

$$AgOH/Ag_2O + e^- \text{ (from reducing agents)} \rightarrow Ag$$

Materials Sucrose, $C_{12}H_{22}O_{11}$ (50 g)
Tartaric acid, $C_4H_6O_6$ (6 g)
Ethanol, C_2H_5OH (100 mL)
Silver Nitrate, $AgNO_3$ (40 g)
Amonium Nitrate, NH_4NO_3 (60 g)
Sodium hydroxide, $NaOH$ (100 g)
Bottle
100-mL Beaker

Safety Precautions Silver nitrate is a corrosive solid and toxic; causes burns; avoid contact with eyes and skin.

Ammonium Nitrate is a strong oxidizer; may explode if heated under confinement; explodes more readily if contaminated with combustible materials; toxic by injestion and inhalation; skin, eye, and respiratory irritant.

Dry silver–ammonium compounds become explosive. **Never** permit the silver compounds to reach dryness. Wash all equipment immediately and thoroughly including the silvered objects with excess clean tap water.

Sodium hydroxide is a corrosive solid; skin burns are possible; significant heat evolves when added to water and solutions are very dangerous to eyes and skin.

Nitric acid is a corrosive strong oxidant and toxic by inhalation. Wear chemical splash goggles, chemical-resistant gloves and a chemical-resistant apron.

Preparation	Prepare 3 solutions:
	Solution I: Dissolve 50 g of sucrose and 6.0 g tartaric acid in about 0.5 L distilled water. Boil the solution, cool and add 100 mL ethanol. Make up to one liter with distilled water.
	Solution II: Dissolve 40 g silver nitrate and 60 g ammonium nitrate in distilled water and dilute to make one liter of solution.
	Solution III: Dissolve 100 g sodium hydroxide in enough water to make one liter of solution. **Caution!** Cool solution before final volume is measured.
	Clean a glass bottle with concentrated nitric acid and rinse well. New bottles work best but still must be cleaned with acid wash. Soda bottles work well but must be thoroughly cleaned. Glass liquor bottles also work, vodka and gin bottles are best.
Demonstration	Clean and rinse the bottles (glass) to be silvered with tap water.
	Caution: do not prepare solution comibinations until needed as reaction will proceed irreversibly.
	Add 20 mL solution I into the bottle. Rotate the bottle to coat the entire inside surface for about one minute. Leave solution I in the bottle.
	Mix 20 mL of solutions II and III. A precipitate will cause darkening of the mixture. Immediately pour this dark mixture into the bottle to be silvered. Cap or stopper the bottle and rotate the bottle again so that the entire inside of the bottle becomes coated with the solutions. The inside surface will gradually be coated with silver. Rotate for at least 5 minutes.
	Empty the mixture and dispose of properly. If you wish to save the silver excess, acidify with HCl and reclaim the precipitate of silver chloride.
	Wash the bottle several times with tap water to remove all traces of the ammonium and silver salts.
	Keep the bottle tightly capped to avoid tarnishing. I have had bottles last as long as five years.
	Note: Adjust volumes of solution up or down for different sizes of bottles. Always keep the same proportions. Suggested amounts; 20 mL for a one liter bottle, half this for a pint bottle and double for a two liter container. Try a test tube too!
Disposal	The silver can be reclaimed from any solutions using Flinn Suggested Disposal Method #11. All solutions can be flushed down the drain with excess water.
Reference	Gerald Blackstone and Walter Rohr; Eastchester High School, NY.

The Light Sensitivity of the Silver Halides

Silver bromide crystals are prepared and then exposed to light to demonstrate their photosensitivity.

Application
Photosensitivity • Redox • Photography

Theory
Photography involves the reduction of silver ions. The process by which the silver bromide is activated is not clearly understood. Black and white photographic film consists of a plastic sheet coated with an emulsion of gelatin and silver bromide crystals.

When the film containing silver bromide is exposed to light, the silver bromide becomes activated. Although the effect is not immediately visible, the changes in the crystals become visible during the developing process. During the developing process, the film is placed in a solution that reduces the silver ions that have been activated by the light, to silver metal. Only the activated silver ions are reduced to silver. The silver bromide that was not exposed to light is not affected. The silver produced develops a dark color.

$$AgBr + C_6H_4(OH)_2 \rightarrow 2Ag + C_6H_4O_2 + 2HBr$$

Where the film has been exposed to more light, more grains of silver bromide are reduced. This makes the film darker. For this reason, the lightest parts of the image will be dark on the film. The film is then placed in a solution called a "fixer". The fixer removes all of the excess silver bromide that wasn't reduced when exposed to light. This solution is said to "fix" the image. After this bath the film is clear wherever it was not exposed to light. It is dark where it was exposed.

Safety Precautions
Silver nitrate is corrosive; causes burns; avoid contact with eyes and skin. Wear chemical splash goggles, chemical-resistant gloves and a chemical-resistant apron.

Materials
Silver nitrate, 1 M, $AgNO_3$ (100 mL)
Sodium bromide, 1 M, NaBr (100 mL)
400-mL Beakers (2)
Ring stand
Filter paper
Funnel holder
Bright lamp
Hot plate
Spatula
Filter funnel
Beaker tongs
Small opaque box, approx. 10×10 cm $\times 3$ cm

Preparation   Prepare and heat the solutions up ahead of time to save some time.

Demonstration   Dim the lights in the room. Heat 100 mL silver nitrate solution on a hot plate. Add 100 mL of hot sodium bromide solution (previously heated). A precipitate forms. Separate the precipitate by filtering.

Spread the precipitate on a filter paper using a spatula.

Divide the crystals into two halves and place on two separate pieces of filter paper.

Cover one half with a small opaque box. Expose the other half to a bright light for a few minutes. Remove the box and compare the two samples. The exposed crystals will have turned dark in color.

Disposal   The silver can be recovered using Flinn Suggested Disposal Method #11 or can be flushed down the drain with excess water.

Electricity from a Fuel Cell

A hydrogen–oxygen fuel cell is used to power a small electric motor.

Application | Fuel Cells • Redox Reactions • Conservation of Energy • Catalysts

Theory | A fuel cell is a voltaic cell that converts chemical energy directly into electrical energy. Fuel cells have the highest rate of efficiency of all sources of energy. In fact, fuel cells can be designed to be almost 100% efficient. In contrast, devices that convert chemical energy into mechanical energy and then to electrical energy are only 30 to 40% efficient. This high rate of efficiency explains their use in NASA's space shuttle and in submarines.

This fuel cell involves a redox reaction. At the hydrogen electrode, hydrogen gas is chemisorbed onto the platinum surface. That is, it forms chemical bonds with the atoms of platinum on the electrode's surface. Upon chemisorption the hydrogen gas dissociates into hydrogen atoms.

$$H_2(g) + Pt(s) \rightleftarrows H - Pt - H$$

As this occurs, some of this hydrogen loses an electron to the metal electrode. Hydrogen atoms that lose electrons combine with the hydroxide ions from the electrolyte to form water. Since hydrogen gas is oxidized at this electrode, the electrode is the anode, and is negatively charged.

$$H - Pt - H + 2OH^- \rightleftarrows 2H_2O + Pt + 2e^-$$

Oxygen gas is reduced at the cathode. Oxygen molecules are chemibsorbed onto the cathode and dissociate into oxygen atoms.

$$O_2(g) + Pt(s) \rightleftarrows O - Pt - O$$

These oxygen atoms capture electrons from the metal electrode, producing chemisorbed oxide ions.

$$O - Pt - O + 4e^- \rightleftarrows O^{-2} - Pt - O^{-2}$$

These react with the water in the electrolyte to form hydroxide ions. Since this electrode loses electrons, it becomes positively charged.

$$O^{-2} - Pt - O^{-2} + 2H_2O(l) \rightleftarrows 4OH^-(aq) + Pt(s)$$

The cell reactions are:

Cathode: $O_2(g) + 2H_2O(l) + 4e^- \rightleftarrows 4OH^-(aq)$

Anode: $2H_2(g) + 4OH^-(aq) \rightleftarrows 4H_2O(l) + 4e^-$

Overall: $2H_2(g) + O_2(g) \rightleftarrows 2H_2O(l)$

This fuel cell will develop a maximum potential of 1 volt.

Safety Precautions

Extreme care should be taken when working with mixtures of concentrated acids. Hydrochloric and nitric acids are both very corrosive to skin and eyes and highly toxic by ingestion or inhalation. Nitric acid is also a strong oxidizer, avoid contact with readily oxidized substances, especially acetic acid. Keep open flames away from oxygen and hydrogen gases.

Materials

Fuel cell housing:
Acrylic plastic sheet, $0.5 \times 10 \times 10$ cm (4)
Hole saw and bits, 6 cm and 8 cm diameter
Electric drill with 1/16, 3/8 and 1/4 inch bits
Acrylic tubing, 3/8 inch o.d., 5 cm lengths (4)
Acrylic cement
Bolts with wing nuts, $3/16 \times 1$ inch (4)

Electrodes:
Rubber gaskets, i.d. = 6 cm and o.d. = 8 cm (made from inner tubing)
Nickel wire, 24 ga (8 m)
Metal snips
Filter paper, 8 cm round

To plate nickel screen:
Hydrochloric acid, conc., HCl (30 mL)
Nitric acid, conc., HNO_3 (10 mL)
Platinum, Pt (0.2g)
Distilled water (50 mL)
100-mL Beaker
30-mL Porcelain evaporating dish
Watch glass to cover evaporating dish
Hot plate
Petri dishes (2)
Ring stand with two clamps
1-volt DC motor
Paper propeller, made from an index card
Sodium hydroxide, 1 M, NaOH (50 mL)
Pipet
Rubber tubing, 3/8 inch O.D, 0.5 m length (4)
Gas washing bottles (2)
Oxygen gas
Hydrogen gas
Voltmeter

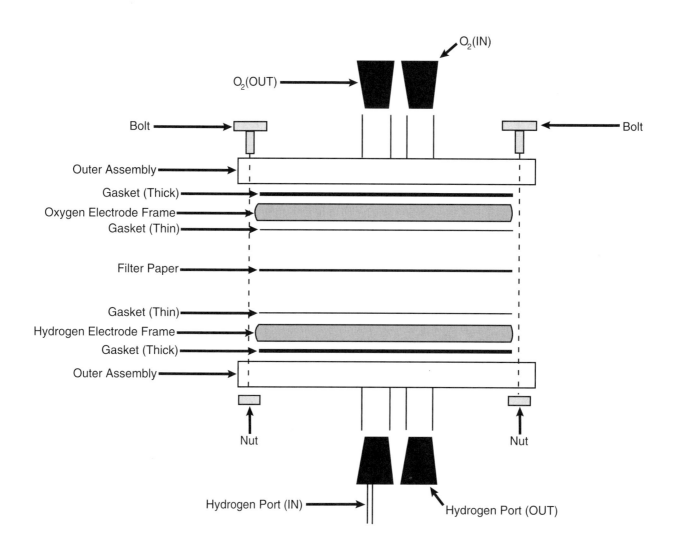

Fuel Cell Assembly

Preparation

Align two acrylic squares on top of each other. Drill two 3/8 inch holes 3 cm apart in the center of both squares. Drill four 1/4 inch holes—one at each corner of the squares. Be sure that all holes are aligned in both squares. Glue four 5-cm pieces of 3/8 inch acrylic tubing to each of the 3/8 inch holes in the squares so one end of the tube is flush with the surface at the acrylic plate.

Center the 8 cm hole saw over the third acrylic square and proceed to cut a hole. Remove the inner hole and cocentrically align the 6 cm hole saw and proceed to cut out the middle. Repeat this procedure with the remaining acrylic square. Using a permanent fine-tipped marker, make approximately 60 evenly-spaced marks around the ring. Drill a 1/16 inch hole through each of these marks. Thread a continuous 4 meter (24 ga) piece of nickel wire such that the final product looks similar to a spoked bicycle wheel. Once wound, allow about 5 cm of wire to extend beyond the edge of the wheel.

Combine 30 mL HCl and 10 mL HNO_3 in a 100 mL beaker in a fume hood. Place 0.2 grams platinum metal in an evaporating dish and add enough of the acid mixture to cover the metal. Cover the dish with a watch glass and heat the dish at approximately 80 °C until the metal dissolves. This will take several hours. After the metal has dissolved, continue heating until all the liquid evaporates. Cool the dish. Dissolve the orange residue in the cooled dish with 50 mL distilled water.

Place each of the nickel frames in separate Petri dishes. Pour the platinum solution [hexachloroplatinate (IV) solution or chloroplatinate acid] over the nickel electrodes. Allow to soak for several hours. The electrodes will develop a spongy black-colored coating of platinum. Swirl the solution periodically to promote an uniform coating of the platinum. Rinse the electrodes and store in distilled water. If stored in distilled water, the electrodes have an indefinite shelf life.

Assemble the fuel cell as indicated on the preceding page.

Demonstration

Through each of the gas ports, moisten the filter paper with sodium hydroxide solution. Clamp the assembly to a ring stand. Use plastic or rubber tubes to connect the hydrogen cylinder to the gas collection bottle and the gas collection bottle to one of the gas ports of the cell. Attach the leads of the motor to the electrodes of the cell. Open the valves of the gases and allow the gas to slowly bubble into the washing bottles. The motor should turn. Allow the apparatus to run a few minutes to allow the potential to stabilize.

Disposal

The acids should be neutralized according to Flinn Suggested Disposal Method #24b before flushing down the drain with excess water. All other solutions can be flushed down the drain with excess water. Save unused hexachloroplatinate (IV) solution and fuel cell for future use.

Reference

Shakhashiri, B. Z. *Chemical Demonstrations*, University of Wisconsin: Madison, WI, 1992; Vol. 4, p. 123.

Oxidation of Magnesium

Magnesium is oxidized in steam to yield hydrogen gas.

Application
Redox • Double Replacement Reactions • Combustion

Theory
Oxidation is defined as an increase in oxidation number which is caused by the loss of electrons or gain of oxygen. Reduction is defined as a decrease in oxidation number caused by the gain of electrons or loss of oxygen. Magnesium is oxidized in steam resulting in the loss of 2 electrons:

$$Mg + H_2O \rightarrow Mg(OH)_2 + H_2$$

In this reaction, hydrogen acts as the oxidizing agent and the magnesium acts as the reducing agent. Hydrogen gas production can be illustrated by burning this flammable gas.

Materials
200-mm Pyrex test tube with stopper
Meker burner
Bunsen burner
Magnesium ribbon, Mg (30 cm)
Test tube holder
Matches

Preparation
Make a 2-mm hole in the test tube—1 cm from bottom. This may be accomplished using a high speed (30,000 rpm) drill with a hobbyist grinding bit. Fire polish the hole. This small hole will make it difficult for the steam to escape and will serve to prevent any other gases from entering the tube. This will ensure that the magnesium is surrounded by a steam atmosphere at all times.

Demonstration
Insert a coil of magnesium a short distance below the hole in the test tube. Tilt the test tube and add approximately 10 mL water to the tube. Careful not to allow any water to escape through the hole. Stopper the tube and clamp it at a 30° angle with the stoppered end down and the small hole at the top.

Heat the water to boiling using the Bunsen burner. The Meker burner is then lit and positioned under the magnesium. The magnesium is heated strongly and begins to burn in the steam.

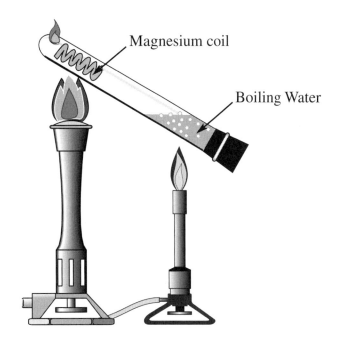

Magnesium coil

Boiling Water

Reference Murray, J. *Science Masters Book,* London, Part II, Series III, p 85.

Chapter 17

Electrochemistry

Electrolytic–Galvanic Demo

A simple, one time approximation of a standard hydrogen electrode is used to show the difference between an electrolytic cell and a galvanic cell.

Application | Electrochemistry • Redox • Activity Series • Nernst Equation

Theory | An electrolytic cell is one that uses an external source of electrical current to drive a redox reaction that will not occur spontaneously. A galvanic cell is one in which a spontaneous oxidation–reduction reaction generates a voltage. Students are introduced to the standard hydrogen electrode via diagram, but seldom by demonstration because they are difficult to assemble. This simple substitute can be used to measure the reduction potential of the $Cl_2(g) / Cl^-(aq)$ system with just a few common materials.

Stage 1 of the demo is an electrolytic cell where HCl solution is subjected to an external voltage. The relevant half reactions are:

$$2\,H^+ + 2\,e^- \rightarrow H_2$$
$$2\,Cl^- \rightarrow Cl_2 + 2\,e^-$$

The reactions occur at a porous carbon electrode, and the gases are adsorbed at their respective electrodes. When the power supply is removed, each electrode now acts as its own half cell in a galvanic cell at which hydrogen is spontaneously oxidized (anode), and chlorine is spontaneously reduced (cathode).

$$H_2 \rightarrow 2\,H^+ + 2e^-$$
$$Cl_2 + 2e^- \rightarrow 2\,Cl^-$$

A voltage very close to the expected 1.36 V for the reduction potential of chlorine is obtained.

Materials | 600-mL Beaker
Hydrogen Chloride, 6M, HCl
Porous carbon rods or strip (2)
3 to 5 V DC power supply
Voltmeter

Safety Precautions | Hydrochloric acid is highly toxic by ingestion or inhalation; severely corrosive to skin and eyes. Chlorine gas is toxic by inhalation or contact, and has a strong, pungent odor. Wear chemical splash goggles, chemical-resistant gloves and a chemical-resistant apron.

Preparation | Prepare or purchase 6 M HCl (513 mL conc. HCl per liter). Add acid to water. Attach connecting wires firmly to the carbon electrodes with clips.

Demonstration

Fill the beaker to about two-thirds capacity with 6 M HCl. Place the carbon rods into the solution. Get them as widely separated as possible and submerged to nearly maximum depth. Connect the wires to the DC power supply and let the electrolysis run slowly for about three to four minutes. Now remove the power supply and replace it with a voltmeter. The system will now operate as a galvanic cell and will read close to 1.36 volts.

This single beaker assembly works well until it becomes contaminated with too much dissolved chlorine. Two beakers of acid connected by a salt bridge will allow multiple class usage. In either case, students can see that the concentrations of the ions are equal, and the partial pressures of the electrogenerated gases are about the same. Hence, the logarithmic concentration term in the Nernst equation becomes zero. Its expression simplifies to:

$$E_{cell} = E°_{cathode} - E°_{anode}$$

Disposal

Neutralize the solution with 1 M sodium carbonate before flushing down the drain with excess water according to Flinn Suggested Disposal Method #24b.

References

Talesnick, I. *Idea Bank Collation,* S 17 Science Supplies and Services: Kingston, Ontario, 1984; Idea #17.

Sears, F. W.; Zemansky, M. W.; Young, H. D. *University Physics 6th ed.,* Addison-Wesley: New York, 1982.

Electrolysis of Water — A Twist

Use the old standby Hoffman apparatus in a slightly different way to allow students to relate equations to experiments.

Application Electrochemistry • Acids and Bases • Electrolysis • Chemical Composition

Theory An aqueous solution of sodium sulfate is subjected to electrolysis. The overall equation for the electrolysis is:

$$2\,H_2O \rightarrow 2H_2 + O_2$$

On the basis of their observations, students can be asked to arrive at the following equations:

$$\text{Anode reaction: } 2\,H_2O \rightarrow O_2 + 4H^+ + 4e^-$$

$$\text{Cathode reaction: } 2\,H_2O + 2e^- \rightarrow H_2 + 2\,OH^-$$

The production of hydrogen ion and hydroxide ion is shown by the use of an indicator.

Materials Hoffman apparatus with Pt electrodes and DC power supply
Sodium sulfate, saturated solution, Na_2SO_4 (500 mL)
600-mL Beaker
Bromothymol blue indicator
Sulfuric acid, 3 M, H_2SO_4
Sodium hydroxide, 3 M, NaOH
Stirring rod250

Safety Precautions Sulfuric acid is severely corrosive to skin and other tissue; considerable heat of dilution with water; even very dilute solutions are harmful to eyes and skin. Solid sodium hydroxide is a corrosive solid; skin burns are possible. Solutions are very dangerous to eyes. The solution process for both substances is highly exothermic. Use only Pyrex® glassware for mixing, and submerge the mixing vessel in an ice bath. Wear chemical splash goggles, chemical-resistant gloves and a chemical-resistant apron.

Preparation Prepare the sodium sulfate solution. Concentration is not critical but use as concentrated a solution as is available to increase the rate of electrolysis. Add enough indicator to the sodium sulfate solution to impart a deep green color. If the solution is blue or yellow, you must adjust the pH to get it green. An easy method is to dip a stirring rod into the sulfuric acid solution (if blue) or the sodium hydroxide solution (if yellow), and then stir the sodium sulfate solution with it. Go back and forth until the green color is definite. You may want students to see this, it might help their understanding later on. Rinse the Hoffman apparatus completely, including the electrodes with the solution, and discard the rinses.

Demonstration

Fill the Hoffman apparatus from the beaker. Save the leftover solution in the beaker. Carry out the electrolysis for about ten minutes, or until the volumes of evolved gases can be easily measured. Shut off the power.

Ask students to record and interpret the following:

1. Colors observed at the two electrodes.

2. The volumes of the two gases collected.

3. The identity of the gases. (Confirm with burning and glowing splints.)

Ask students to write balanced "half reactions" for each electrode. (See above.) Ask them to predict the relative amounts of acid and base produced and therefore the color of the resulting solution when it is all poured back into the beaker. (They will most likely predict yellow based on the half-reaction equations.)

Finally, pour all of the remaining solution out of the apparatus back into the original beaker and discuss why it is GREEN!!! To balance the electrons, the cathode reaction has to be doubled, resulting in equal quantities of hydrogen and hydroxide ion produced.

Disposal

The solution can be flushed down the sink with excess water.

References

Talesnick, I. *Idea Bank Collation;* S 17 Science Supplies and Service: Kingston, Ontario, 1984; Idea #196.

The Science Teacher **1975,** *42 (5),* 31.

A Homemade Battery

Produce a simple battery from ordinary laboratory supplies and show the difference between a battery and a cell.

Application Electrochemistry • Redox • Consumer Chemistry

Theory Two different metals in an electrolyte solution can produce a galvanic cell which will light a flashlight bulb. Two or more of these cells connected together produce a battery. Six of the cells connected in series will operate a transistor radio, which requires 9 volts. The relevant half reactions are:

$$Mg(s) \rightarrow Mg^{2+}(aq) + 2e^- \quad E° = 2.37 \text{ V}$$
$$Cu^{2+}(aq) + 2e^- \rightarrow Cu(s) \quad E° = 0.34 \text{ V}$$

The E° for the cell would therefore be 2.71 V.

Materials Gas collecting jars (one for each cell)
1 hole rubber stoppers to fit the jars
Cupric sulfate, 0.5 M, $CuSO_4$
Sodium sulfate, 0.5 M, Na_2SO_4
Magnesium ribbon, Mg
Copper metal strip or wire, Cu
Insulated wire for connections
Dialysis tubing

Safety Precautions Cupric sulfate is toxic by ingestion and inhalation, and a skin and respiratory irritant. Wear chemical splash goggles, chemical-resistant gloves and a chemical-resistant apron.

Preparation Prepare the solutions as follows: 0.5 M, $CuSO_4$, 125 g of cupric sulfate pentahydrate per liter of solution: 0.5 M Na_2SO_4, 161 grams of sodium sulfate decahydrate crystal per liter of solution or 71 g of the anhydrous reagent per liter of solution. Polish the metals with fine sandpaper or steel wool to get a fairly clean surface. Tie a knot in one end of the dialysis tubing.

Demonstration Fill the gas jar about 2/3 full of the sodium sulfate solution. Bend the magnesium strip into a "J" shape and hang it over the side of the jar into the sodium sulfate solution. Fill the dialysis tubing 2/3 full of the cupric sulfate solution and insert the copper metal strip so that about 2 cm protrudes from the open end of the tubing. Hang the dialysis tubing assembly in the jar on the opposite side from the magnesium strip. Insert the stopper into the jar to hold the assemblies in place. Connect the cell to a flashlight bulb and it should light. If six cells are connected in series, they will power a typical transistor radio.

Disposal | The solution can be disposed of by flushing down the drain with excess water.

References | Talesnick, I. *Idea Bank Collation;* S 17 Science Supplies and Services: Kingston, Ontario, 1984; Idea #349.

The Science Teacher, **1978,** *45 (4),* 51.

The "Standard Orange Electrode"

Present the idea of a reference electrode using an unconventional example.

Application | Electrochemistry • Standard Cell Potentials • Standard Electrodes • Redox

Theory | The electrode potential of a conductive solid in contact with a conductive solution is a relative quantity determined by a difference in electron energies between the substances. It is not possible to measure this difference directly. Another conductive probe (electrode) must be used. Since this probe has its own characteristic potential, a measurement of the energy difference between the electrodes (potential difference or voltage) is actually the difference in the differences! The energy (potential) of one electrode differs from the solution by a certain amount, for example:

$$\Delta E_1 = E_{electrode\ 1} - E_{solution}$$

The potential of the other electrode differs from the solution by

$$\Delta E_2 = E_{electrode\ 2} - E_{solution}$$

The measured potential between the electrodes is $\Delta E = \Delta E_1 - \Delta E_2$. For this reason, all measurements of electrode potentials are relative, and make sense only if the nature of the reference electrode is reported.

The fundamental reference electrode is the standard hydrogen electrode, assigned a value of 0 volts. Other reference electrodes such as the standard calomel electrode are common. This demonstration uses a rather uncommon standard electrode, a graphite rod imbedded in an orange, but the concept is the same. The standard electrode is assigned a value of 0 volts, and the potentials of the other electrodes are measured relative to the standard.

Materials | Zinc nitrate, 1.0 M, $Zn(NO_3)_2$ (100 mL)
Cupric nitrate, 1.0 M, $Cu(NO_3)_2$ (100 mL)
Lead nitrate, 1.0 M, $Pb(NO_3)_2$ (100 mL)
Sodium chloride, 1.0 M, NaCl (100 mL)
250-mL Beaker (3)
U-tube
Cotton plugs for the ends of the U-tube (2)
Large orange
Zinc strip, Zn
Copper strip, Cu
Lead strip, Pb
Carbon rod, C
Voltmeter
Sodium sulfide, Na_2S, for disposal of the lead nitrate (25 g)

Safety Precautions

Nitrates are strong oxidants, fire risks when in contact with organic material. Lead, copper, and zinc nitrates are toxic by ingestion or inhalation. Sodium sulfide is a flammable solid, skin irritant and liberates toxic hydrogen sulfide on contact with acids. Wear chemical splash goggles, chemical-resistant gloves and a chemical-resistant apron.

Preparation

Fill the U-tube with the NaCl solution and plug the ends with cotton. Check for leaks. Wad the cotton more tightly if needed. Roll the orange on a hard surface to break some of the internal membranes. Cut two 1-cm holes in the orange (cork borer works well). Insert the carbon rod in one hole. Label the three beakers for the different nitrate solutions and add the 100 mL of the appropriate solution to each beaker.

Demonstration

Set the zinc nitrate beaker next to the orange. Invert the salt bridge and insert one end into the beaker and the other end into the remaining hole in the orange. Be sure that the cotton plugs are making contact with the juice in the orange and with the solution in the beaker. Insert the zinc strip in the beaker and attach the voltmeter wires. Attach the black (the common or negative) wire to the carbon rod in the orange and attach red (positive) wire to the zinc strip. Record the voltage. It will be negative! If the voltmeter cannot read negative voltages directly, reverse the wires between the carbon and the zinc. Record this new voltage as negative.

Repeat the procedure with the other beakers and metal strips. Record the voltages in the same way.

Now ask students to predict the results of connecting the different metal half cells with each other. Remove the orange and replace it with the appropriate half cell to verify. Don't forget the salt bridge.

Disposal

The zinc and copper nitrate solutions can be disposed of by flushing down the drain with excess water. The lead nitrate solutions must be precipitated using Flinn Suggested Disposal Method #27f.

Reference

Shakhashiri, B. Z. *Chemical Demonstrations;* University of Wisconsin: Madison, WI, 1992; Vol. 4; p 107.

A Copper–Magnesium Cell

Demonstrate a galvanic cell in which the same electrode acts as both anode and cathode.

Application

Electrochemistry • Redox

Theory

Electrical energy can be extracted from the reaction between magnesium and acid. In most voltaic cells, the oxidation and reduction processes must be separated in order to force electric current through an external circuit. In this cell, when the magnesium is immersed in the acid, it reacts directly, and both oxidation and reduction occur at the surface of the magnesium. It is both anode and cathode.

$$\text{Oxidation: } Mg(s) \rightarrow Mg^{2+}(aq) + 2e^-$$

$$\text{Reduction: } 2\,H^+(aq) + 2e^- \rightarrow H_2(g)$$

The copper acts as an auxiliary electrode. Some reduction of the hydrogen ion also occurs there.

The two electrodes are dipped into 12 M sulfuric acid and then into 1M hydrochloric acid. The lamp burns more brightly in the HCl solution. The electrode potential is greater in the HCl also. The differences can only be due to differences in the conductivity of the acid solutions. Magnesium probably reacts faster with the 1 M HCl than with the 12 M sulfuric acid. This is likely due to the greater degree of ionization in the dilute solution and results in a higher rate of electron release to the circuit.

Materials

Hydrochloric acid, 1 M, HCl (150 mL)
Sulfuric acid, 12 M, H_2SO_4 (150 mL)
Copper strip, Cu
Magnesium strip, Mg
250-mL Beakers (2)
Voltmeter
2.4 V Flashlight bulb with socket
Connecting wires

Safety Precautions

Hydrochloric acid is highly toxic by ingestion or inhalation; severely corrosive to skin and eyes. Sulfuric acid is severely corrosive to eyes, skin and other tissue; considerable heat of dilution with water; even very dilute solutions are harmful to eyes and skin. Wear chemical splash goggles, chemical-resistant gloves and a chemical-resistant apron.

Preparation

Prepare acid solutions or purchase from Flinn Scientific. To prepare 12 M H_2SO_4, place 300 grams of ice in a 2-liter beaker. Place the beaker in an ice bath. Slowly add 640 mL of concentrated sulfuric acid. This mixture will get very hot. **Wear Safety Goggles!** When the mixture cools, dilute it to a volume of 1 liter with distilled water. Label the beakers for the acid solution. Attach the wires to the lamp socket and insert the bulb. Attach the other end of the wires to the copper and the magnesium strips.

Demonstration

Add 150 mL of the acid solution to the appropriately labeled beaker. Immerse the two metal strips in the sulfuric acid solution and check the voltage. Remove the electrodes, rinse well, and then immerse them into the hydrochloric acid. The lamp will glow brighter. Check the voltage again, it will be higher.

Disposal

Neutralize acids with sodium carbonate according to Flinn Suggested Disposal Method #24b before flushing solutions down the drain with excess water.

References

Alyea, H. N.; Dutton, F. B. *Tested Demonstrations in Chemical Education;* Journal of Chemistry: Easton, Pa, 1965, p 17.

Shakhashiri, B. Z. *Chemical Demonstrations,* University of Wisconsin: Madison, WI, 1992; Vol. 4, p 137.

Constructing a Dry Cell

Illustrate the construction of a common dry cell battery.

Application | Electrochemistry • Redox • Consumer Chemistry

Theory | The term "dry cell" is a misnomer. The cell is not free of water, rather, it is called a dry cell because it does not contain any fluids. The water in the electrolyte is absorbed into a felt pad to keep it from flowing. It is also known as a carbon–zinc battery, since these materials are used for the electrodes. While the zinc electrode is active, and is consumed during the cell operation, the carbon electrode is actually inert. Electrons are supplied by the oxidation of zinc. The reduction process involves manganese dioxide, and occurs at the carbon electrode. The relevant half-reactions are:

$$\text{Anode:} \quad Zn(s) \rightarrow Zn^{2+}(aq) + 2e^-$$

$$\text{Cathode:} \quad MnO_2(s) + H_2O(l) + e^- \rightarrow MnO(OH)(s) + OH^-(aq)$$

Materials | Ammonium chloride, 4 M, NH_4Cl
Manganese dioxide, MnO_2 (4 g)
Zinc metal foil, $12 \times 12 \times 0.25$ mm
Felt pad, 12×12 mm
Carbon rod (15 cm long and 6 to 10 mm dia.)
String
Voltmeter
Connecting wires
Battery operated clock

Safety Precautions | Ammonium chloride is toxic by ingestion. Manganese dioxide is moderately toxic, a strong oxidizing agent; avoid contact with organic materials. Do not allow the felt pad to dry out while in contact with manganese dioxide. Wear chemical splash goggles, chemical-resistant gloves and a chemical-resistant apron.

Preparation | Attach the connecting wires to the battery terminals on the clock. Mix the ammonium chloride solution by using 21.4 g of reagent for 100 mL solution. Wearing gloves, saturate the felt pad with the ammonium chloride solution, squeezing out the excess.

Demonstration | Sprinkle the manganese dioxide onto the damp felt pad in a thin layer. Wrap the pad around the carbon rod, with the MnO_2 in contact with the carbon. Wrap the zinc foil tightly around the pad, making sure that the zinc does not touch the carbon rod. Tie with a string. Press one voltmeter probe to the zinc and the other to the carbon. Record the voltage. Attach the positive lead from the clock to the carbon rod, and the negative lead to the zinc. The clock will start and should continue to run for about a half-hour.

Disposal The zinc can be rinsed, dried and re-used. Rinse the felt pad under running water to remove the manganese dioxide. It can be saved for re-use or discarded in the trash. Ammonium chloride solution can be flushed down the drain with excess water.

References Shakhashiri, B.Z. *Chemical Demonstrations;* University of Wisconsin: Madison, WI, 1992; Vol. 4, p 111.

Huheey, J.E. *Inorganic Chemistry* 2nd. ed.; **1978,** p 314.

Graphite Electrodes

Pencil "leads" are actually a graphite/clay composition that will serve as perfectly good electrodes for student electrolysis experiments.

Application	Electrochemistry • Redox • Electrolysis
Theory	The graphite in pencil "leads" allows their use as inexpensive carbon electrodes for student electrolysis labs. The relevant half-reactions are as follows:

$$\text{Anode reaction:} \quad 2\,Cl^-(aq) \rightarrow Cl_2(g) + 2e^-$$

$$\text{Cathode reaction:} \quad Cu^{2+}(aq) + 2e^- \rightarrow Cu(s)$$

Materials	(Per student pair for an experiment): Wooden pencils (2) Battery holder with two AA dry cells Wires and alligator clips 50-mL Beaker Cupric chloride, 1 M, $CuCl_2$ (10 mL)
Safety Precautions	Cupric chloride is toxic by ingestion and inhalation. Chlorine gas is produced in this reaction, which is a severe irritant and toxic by inhalation. Wear chemical splash goggles and always follow laboratory safety rules while performing demonstrations.
Preparation	Sharpen the pencils and carefully strip a few more millimeters of the wood away from the points. Using a knife or single edge razor blade, cut a "V" shaped groove around the diameter of each pencil about 5 cm above the point. Deepen this groove until the pencil lead is exposed and the groove is wide enough to allow the jaws of the alligator clip to contact the lead. Attach the other ends of the wire to the battery holder terminals.
Demonstration	Add the cupric chloride solution to the beaker and immerse the electrodes. Students will be able to see bubbles of chlorine gas from the sharp point at the anode, and the cathode will get a reddish-brown coating of copper metal. This will also allow students to experience the odor of chlorine gas in small enough quantities that no real danger exists. Rinse the electrodes after use with distilled or de-ionized water.
Disposal	Excess solutions may be stored or disposed of by flushing down a drain with excess water.
References	Talesnick, I. *Idea Bank Collation;* S 17 Science Supplies and Services: Kingston, Ontario, 1984; Idea #252.

The Earth Cell

Demonstrate an electrochemical cell made with everyday components.

Application	Electrochemistry • Redox
Theory	Carbon and aluminum electrodes are used in combination with wet leaves, pond mud or other similar damp organic material to produce an electrochemical cell with an output of around 0.25 volts. The relevant reactions are:

$$\text{Anode:} \quad Al(s) \rightarrow Al_3^+(aq) + 3e^-$$

$$\text{Cathode:} \quad 2\,H_2O + 2e^- \rightarrow 2\,OH^- + H_2$$

	The decomposing plant matter produces a slightly acidic environment which is sufficient to act as the electrolyte.
Materials	Aluminum strip, Al Carbon or graphite rod, C Connecting wires 250-mL beaker Voltmeter 1.5V lightbulb and socket
Safety Precautions	Wear chemical splash goggles and always follow laboratory safety rules while performing demonstrations.
Preparation	Polish the surface of the aluminum strip with sandpaper or fine steel wool. Attach the connecting wires to the electrodes.
Demonstration	Place the electrodes in the beaker on opposite sides. Fill the space between them with the damp organic material. If you are using wet leaves, they work better if some decomposition has begun. You may have to add some tap water to get good contact between the electrolyte and the electrodes. Make sure that the electrodes are not touching each other. Attach the wires to the lightbulb socket. The bulb should glow faintly. Use the voltmeter probes to measure the output voltage of the cell.
Disposal	Materials can be saved for reuse or disposed of in the trash.
References	Talesnick, I. *Idea Bank Collation;* S 17 Science Supplies and Services: Kingston, Ontario, 1984; Idea #590. *The Crucible,* **1978,** IX(2), 17.

Gravity Cell

Use density differences between two solutions in the construction of a galvanic cell.

Application | Electrochemistry • Redox • Density

Theory | The cell is called a gravity cell because it is a voltaic cell in which the anode and cathode half cells are separated only by the difference in the densities of the solutions. It is also known as a Daniell cell. The cathode is copper metal suspended in a 1M cupric sulfate solution and the anode is zinc metal suspended in 0.01M zinc sulfate solution. This is much less dense than the cupric sulfate solution, so it floats on top of the cupric sulfate. No salt bridge is needed since the two solutions are in contact.

The half-cell reactions are:

$$\text{Cathode:} \quad Cu^{2+}(aq) + 2e^- \rightarrow Cu(s)$$
$$\text{Anode:} \quad Zn(s) \rightarrow Zn^{2+}(aq) + 2e^-$$

Materials | Copper sheet, $10 \times 30 \times 0.25$ mm
Zinc sheet, $10 \times 30 \times 0.8$ mm
Cupric sulfate 1.0 M, $CuSO_4$ (500 mL)
Zinc sulfate, 0.01 M, $ZnSO_4$ (500 mL)
2-liter Beaker
DC motor which operates on 0.5 volts
Stand and clamp for motor
500-mL long-stem separatory funnel or filter funnel
Card stock propeller and glue

Safety Precautions | Cupric sulfate is a skin and respiratory irritant and toxic by ingestion and inhalation. Zinc sulfate is a skin and mucous membrane irritant. Wear chemical splash goggles and always follow laboratory safety rules while performing demonstrations.

Preparation | Prepare the 1 M cupric sulfate solution by using 250 g $CuSO_4 \cdot 5H_2O$ per liter of solution and the 0.01 M zinc sulfate by adding 2.9 g $ZnSO_4 \cdot 7H_2O$ per liter of solution. Use tin snips to cut an electrode to the indicated shape from the copper sheet and another from the zinc sheet.

Bend the long tab on each electrode so that it is perpendicular to the disk. Position the copper electrode in the beaker so that the disk is parallel with and about 2 cm above the bottom. Bend the tab over the rim of the beaker to hold it in place. Position the zinc electrode in the beaker with its disk parallel to and about 4 cm above the copper disk. Bend the tab over the rim on the opposite side of the beaker. Remove both electrodes carefully. Mount the motor in its clamp and glue the card stock propeller to the shaft. Fill the separatory funnel with the copper sulfate solution. If using a filter funnel, put a small plug of cotton into the top of the stem.

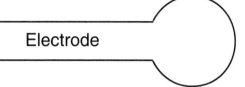

Electrode

Demonstration

Position the electrodes in the beaker as before. Be sure that they do not touch. Pour just enough of the zinc sulfate solution into the beaker to cover the copper electrode—about 2 cm. Insert the stem of the funnel along the side of the beaker and **slowly** add the copper sulfate solution. It must flow slowly to create as little turbulence or mixing as possible. Add enough to lift the interface with the zinc sulfate solution to a point about halfway between the electrodes. Clip a motor lead to each electrode. If the motor does not start immediately, it may need a nudge on the propeller to overcome inertia.

Disposal

Solutions can be disposed by flushing down the drain with excess water.

References

Shakhashiri, B. Z. *Chemical Demonstrations;* University of Wisconsin: Madison, WI, 1992; Vol. 4, p 119.

Skinner, J. F. *J. Chem. Ed.* **1977,** *54,* 619.

Chapter 18

Polymer Chemistry

Polyurethane Foam

A foamed polymer is formed by combining two liquids.

Application   Polymers • Organic Chemistry • Consumer Chemistry

Theory   Liquid A is usually a polyether alcohol and liquid B contains a polyfunctional isocyanate. Liquid A contains a blowing agent which is often a freon type material that vaporizes when A and B react exothermically. Much of the volume increase is due to the expansion of the blowing agent. Typically, the volume increase in this type of reaction is a factor of 30 or more. The polyurethane is an elimination polymer; when two monomers react a molecule of CO_2 or H_2O is eliminated. Polyurethane foams are used in furniture, packaging, insulation and flotation devices.

Materials   *Polyurethane Foam System,* available from Flinn, CO335
Latex gloves
Small plastic cups (2)
Wooden stirrer

Safety Precautions   Wear chemical splash goggles, chemical resistant-gloves, and a chemical-resistant apron. Avoid contact with skin and mucous membranes. Work in a fume hood or a well ventilated area. Avoid breathing any of the vapors. Do not ingest any of the materials and use them only in the manner for which they are intended. Wash hands thoroughly when finished.

Demonstration   The system contains two liquids, usually referred to as liquid A and liquid B. Measure out equal volumes of the two liquids and mix them in a suitable container. A clear plastic cup or other clear container allows the process to be seen easily, but as a change of pace—try using a latex glove or a balloon. Mix the liquids and stir until the mixture begins expanding. Do not disturb until it has cured.

Disposal   The disposable cups may be thrown in the trash. Any glass equipment will need to be cleaned by using small amounts of acetone in a fume hood. Any leftover liquids should be mixed together, allowed to react, and then disposed of in the trash.

Reference   Shakhashiri, B. Z. *Chemical Demonstrations,* University of Wisconsin: Madison, WI, 1983; Vol. 1, p 216.

Reduction of a Polymer

Foamed polymers can be dramatically dissolved using common organic solvents.

Application | Polymers • Organic Chemistry

Theory | Acetone dissolves polystyrene causing the foaming agent (butane or pentane) to escape. As the polymer dissolves, the rigid form appears to melt into a puddle of goo. As the acetone evaporates, the polymer will reappear and can be recycled into other products. Polystyrene is also used in CD or audio cassette cases, and many other commercial products. Styrofoam® is Dow Chemical's trade name for its polystyrene products.

Materials | 150-mL Beaker
Acetone (50 mL)
Polystyrene, packing peanuts (50 liters)

Optional:
   Polystyrene wig stand
   Acetone (250 mL)
   Glass or aluminum pie plate
   Hot plate

Safety Precautions | Acetone is flammable, a dangerous fire risk and toxic by ingestion and inhalation. The acetone–polymer mixture is also flammable. Wear chemical splash goggles, chemical-resistant gloves and a chemical-resistant apron.

Caution: If acetone is to be warmed, use **only** a hot plate or a warm (40 °C) water bath. Avoid open flames.

Demonstration | Pour 50 mL of acetone into a 150-mL beaker. Introduce some foam "packing peanuts" into the beaker. The peanuts will appear to dissolve into the acetone releasing a gas. It is possible to reduce a large volume of these peanuts at a time (about 50 liters of packing peanuts).

Place a polystyrene wig stand in a large glass dish. Pour warmed acetone over the polystyrene. The polystyrene will appear to dissolve and the "wig head" will lose its form resulting in a blob of styrene. This demonstration is great at Halloween. Possibly retitle the demo—"The Wicked Witch Melts Away!"

Disposal | Allow the acetone–polystyrene mixture to evaporate in the hood overnight, then dispose of the solids in the trash.

Latex Polymer

A rubber ball is formed from a latex solution.

Application | Polymers • Organic Chemistry

Theory | Latex is a white, sticky, aqueous suspension of a hydrocarbon polymer that is naturally occuring or man-made. Natural latex was the only source of rubber until 1945. Latex is a colloidal dispersion of rubber particles coated with a protein. The protein coating is responsible for keeping the rubber emulsified.

When an acid is added to latex, the proteins are hydrolyzed and the rubber particles coagulate. The rubber particles still contain active sites and upon agglomeration additional carbon–carbon bonds are formed resulting in some cross-linking and polymer chain extension.

Materials | Latex (50 mL)
Acetic acid or common white vinegar, 1 M (500 mL)
600-mL Beaker
Latex gloves
Ziplock® bag

Safety Precautions | Wear safety goggles. Use protective gloves as indicated. The acetic acid solution is fairly low concentration, but it can be a skin irritant. Keep latex mixture away from clothing, it is difficult to remove.

Demonstration | Pour 50 mL of latex into 500 mL of 1 M acetic acid. The latex will cross-link in the acetic acid and produce a rubber-like material. Wearing a protective glove, squeeze the acetic acid out of the latex and mold it into a ball. The polymer can also be easily formed within a large Ziplock bag.

Disposal | Solutions can be flushed down the drain with excess water.

Reference | David Katz, Cabrini College, Radner, PA.

Make a polymer from Elmer's® Glue.

Application Polymers • Organic Chemistry

Theory The reaction between borax and Elmer's Glue involves cross-linking the casein protein molecules in the glue. The reaction occurs at the surface of the glue mass, so kneading the mass with your fingers will assist in mixing and getting complete cross-linking. The differences in the polymer types are probably due to the degree of cross-linking that can be achieved.

Materials Elmer's Glue
Sodium tetraborate, sat. solution, $Na_2B_4O_7 \cdot 10H_2O$
600-mL Beaker
Ziplock® bag
Liquid laundry starch

Safety Precautions Borax, (sodium tetraborate) is toxic by ingestion and inhalation. Wear chemical splash goggles and always follow laboratory safety rules while performing demonstrations.

Demonstration **To form a rigid polymer:** Mix equal volumes of Elmer's Glue and saturated borax solution in a beaker. Work the mass with your fingers to get maximum contact between the solutions. Wear plastic gloves to keep clean up simple.

To form a slime-type polymer: Mix equal volumes of the glue and liquid laundry starch in a Ziplock bag, seal and work thoroughly with your fingers.

Disposal All materials can be thrown in the trash.

Reference Woodrow Wilson, Chem 5 Institute.

Superabsorbant Polymers

Solidify water with only a few grams of a "magic" polymer.

Application Polymers • Organic Chemistry • Osmotic Pressure

Theory Superabsorbant polymers were originally created to deal with such problems as to remove moisture from automobile and jet fuels and as an absorbent for moisture in grain storage facilities. Today these polymers are used in such household products as diapers and as a water retainer in potting soil. Sodium polyacrylate is manufactured by polymerizing sodium acrylate and acrylic acid. It has an ability to absorb more than 800 times its weight in distilled water.

The absorption of water in sodium polyacrylate occurs because of the difference of sodium concentration between the water and the polymer. The polymer membrane is only permeable to water. Osmotic pressure causes the water to flow into the sodium-rich polymer in order to establish an equilibrium of sodium ion concentration within and outside the polymer. Distilled water should be used since tap water has a high electrolytic concentration, which greatly reduces the amount of water absorbed.

Salt may be added to the gelled polymer. As the concentration of sodium ions increase outside the polymer, the water will flow out of the polymer network resulting in a solution of the polymer in salt water.

Materials 400-mL Beakers (2)
Distilled water
Sodium polyacrylate
Table salt, NaCl

Safety Precautions Wear chemical splash goggles and always follow laboratory safety rules while performing demonstrations.

Demonstration Add 0.5 grams of sodium polyacrylate to a 400-mL beaker. Fill a second 400-mL beaker with distilled water and add a few drops of food coloring for contrast. Pour the colored water into the sodium polyacrylate. Pour the mixture back into the second beaker. The polymer should absorb the water immediately producing a gel-like material.

To reduce the gel into a solution add a few grams of salt.

An alternative demonstration is to use a nontransparent plastic bottle. Pour distilled water into the bottle containing the polymer and tip it upside down. Add salt, allow water to pour out. Ask class to explain.

Disposal All solutions may be flushed down a sink with excess water.

Reference Institute for Chemical Education, University of Wisconsin: Madison, Summer 1989.

Slime

Have fun preparing slime, a non-Newtonian liquid.

Application	Polymers • Organic Chemistry • Consumer Chemistry
Theory	The guar gum is used as a thickener in foods. Tetraborate ions in borax causes a cross linking of the guar gum chains producing a non-Newtonian type of fluid. The fluid flows slowly but breaks when pulled on rapidly.
	The water soluble fraction (85%) of guar flour is called guaran. Guaran is the principle polysaccharide from the endosperm of guar seeds.
Materials	Guar gum, available from Flinn, G0038 Borax, laundry borax is acceptable Containers, plastic cups are OK Sticks to stir Distilled water Food Coloring
Safety Precautions	Wear chemical splash goggles and always follow laboratory safety rules while performing demonstrations. Never eat food in a chemistry lab. Once a food product is brought into a lab it is considered contaminated and not safe for consumption.
Preparation	Prepare a saturated borax solution (4%) by placing a handful of the borax into a 1-liter soda bottle, properly labeled and filled with distilled water. This should serve as a one-year supply.
Demonstration	While stirring vigorously, slowly add 3 to 4 g guar gum powder to 500 mL distilled water. Add a few drops of food coloring if available, and stir. Stir in about 20 mL of saturated borax solution with gusto.
	Note: The quantities of the reactants are not critical but approximate. Vigorous stirring is essential.
	The product may develop mold in a few days (it is a food product!).
	Do not allow slime to remain on clothing, upholstery, or wood surfaces—it will stain.
Disposal	Liquids may be disposed of by flushing down a sink with excess water. Solids may be disposed of in a trash container.

Inorganic Polymer

Polymers need not be organic—inorganic polymers also exist.

Application

Polymers • Organic Chemistry • Periodicity

Theory

Polymers are very large molecules formed by the covalent bonding of repeating small molecules, known as monomers. Polymers are usually organic due to the four available bonds in carbon; however, silicon also has four available bonds and may form polymer-like molecules. Silicon dioxide, or silica occurs widely in nature as sand, quartz, flint or diatomite. Other forms, such as fumed silica or silica gel are widely used in commerical products. The acidification of sodium silicate is hydrated silica or silicic acid ($SiO_2 \cdot xH_2O$).

Materials

Sodium silicate, saturated solution, $Na_2SiO_3 \cdot 9H_2O$ (50 mL)
Acetic acid or household vinegar, 1M, CH_3CO_2H (25 mL)
Ziplock® bag
Food coloring

Optional:
    Solution A: 25 g sodium silicate solution and 25 mL water
    Solution B: 18 mL 95% ethanol and 7 mL water

Safety Precautions

Wear chemical splash goggles and always follow laboratory safety rules while performing demonstrations. The polymer may be handled without gloves.

Demonstration

Pour 50 mL saturated sodium silicate solution into a zip-lock plastic bag. Add 25 mL acetic acid. Work the mixture thoroughly with your fingers until the mixture has completely polymerized. Remove the mass from the bag and form it into a ball. Food coloring may be added to the sodium silicate solution for color.

Alternate Demonstration

Mix solutions A and B together, stir. Decant any liquid portion and dump the white solid onto a generous layer of paper towels. Squeeze the white solid into a ball form. The ball of polymer will bounce quite nicely. If thrown against a wall, it will splatter like a snowball. Please use caution.

Disposal

Solutions may be flushed down a sink with plenty of water and all solids may be disposed of in the trash.

Reference

Cole, J. W. *J. Chem. Ed.* **1946.**

Production of Nylon

Recreate the historic discovery of nylon.

Application

Polymers • Consumer Chemistry • Organic Chemistry

Theory

Nylon was first produced by the condensation of sebacyl chloride and 1,6-diamino-hexane. It works equally well with adipoyl chloride.

The condensation occurs at the surface of an aqueous layer and a non-aqueous layer producing the condensation polymer and hydrogen chloride. The faster the polymer is removed, the faster more is formed. Hence the concept of a rope. The rope is formed as the polymer is lifted from the surface. The rope is essentially a hollow tube of interfacial polycondensate product.

Traditionally the two solutions had to be prepared from pure ingredients. All necessary solutions are presently available pre-mixed from regular school lab suppliers.

Materials

Mystery Nylon Factor, Flinn Demo Kit AP2088
    or
Hexamethylenediamine/sodium hydroxide solution
Sebacoyl chloride or adipoyl chloride/hexane solution
Paper clip
50-mL Beaker
Paper tube (from paper towels or aluminum foil, etc.)

Safety Precautions

Hexamethylenediamine/sodium hydroxide solution is toxic by ingestion and a strong tissue irritant. The sebacoyl chloride/hexane solution is a flammable liquid. Adipoyl chloride/hexane solution is a flammable liquid and toxic by ingestion and inhalation. Wear chemical splash goggles, chemical-resistant gloves and a chemical-resistant apron.

Demonstration

Pour about 10 to 15 mL of the aqueous diamine solution into the beaker.
Carefully pour the same amount of the hexane/chloride solution on top.
Using the paper clip bent as a hook, snag the interface and lift carefully to obtain the "nylon rope". Continue lifting the rope until it breaks or until one of the reactants is totally consumed.

Students with gloves may want to help remove the rope across the room to see how long of a piece may be formed. Winding the rope around a paper towel tube will help.

Disposal

The nylon produced may be washed and dried, then disposed of in the trash.

Reference

Alyea, H. N.; Dutton, F. B. *Tested Demonstrators in Chemistry;* 6th ed., Journal of Chemical Education: Easton, PA, 1965; p 136.

Thiokol — A Sulfur Polymer

Demonstrate formation of an organic sulfide polymer.

Application | Organic Chemistry • Polymers

Theory | The reaction is a linear chain polymerization. The polymer forms rapidly at the temperature used. The reaction is as follows:

$$Cl-CH_2-CH_2-Cl \quad + \quad Na^+S-SNa^+ \rightarrow$$
1,2-Dichloroethane   Sodium Polysulfide

$$-(CH_2-CH_2-S-S-CH_2-CH_2-S-S-)_n + NaCl$$
Thiokol

Materials | Sulfur powder, S (6 g)
250-mL Beakers, (2)
Sodium hydroxide, 1.0 M, NaOH (100 mL)
Hot plate
Thermometer
25-mL Graduated cylinder
Stirring rod
1,2-Dichloroethane, $C_2H_4Cl_2$ (20 mL)

Safety Precautions | Solid sodium hydroxide is a corrosive solid; skin burns are possible. Solutions are very dangerous to eyes. 1,2-dichloroethane is flammable; toxic by ingestion, inhalation, and skin absorption, a strong skin and eye irritant and an alleged animal carcinogen. Sulfur may be a skin irritant and is a fire risk when finely divided. When sulfur is burned, toxic sulfur dioxide is produced. This reaction is best done in a fume hood. Wear chemical splash goggles, chemical-resistant gloves and a chemical-resistant apron.

Preparation | Heat 6 g sulfur and 100 mL of 1 M NaOH in a 250-mL beaker, using a hot plate. Heat to boiling, stirring constantly, and allow to boil for 5 minutes. A deep red solution of sodium polysulfide should result. Allow to cool, and decant into a clean 250-mL beaker.

Demonstration | Heat the polysulfide solution to 90 °C on the hot plate. Slowly add the 20 mL of dichloroethane with constant stirring, forming a milky suspension. Remove from the heat, since the reaction is very exothermic, and continue stirring until a mass of yellow thiokol polymer forms. Remove the polymer with forceps and wash with water.

Disposal | The solid products can be disposed of in the trash and the solutions flushed down the drain with excess water.

Reference | Alyea, H. N.; Dutton, F. B., *Tested Demonstrations in Chemistry;* 6th ed.; Journal of Chemical Education: Easton, PA, 1965.

Skewering a Balloon

Demonstrate how a needle can pierce a balloon without popping it.

Application
Polymers • Organic Chemistry

Theory
Balloons are made out of rubber or latex. The thin sheets consist of long, intertwined strands of polymer molecules. These polymer chains have a degree of elasticity, and so the material is elastic. When the balloon is inflated, the polymer strands are stretched, but more so on the middle of the balloon than on the ends. A sharp, lubricated point can be pushed through the strands at the nipple or tie ends of the balloon because the polymer strands are capable of stretching around it. If this is tried at the middle of the balloon, where the polymer strands are already greatly stretched, they will break, resulting in popping of the balloon. The tear will rapidly enlarge as the air rushes out of the balloon.

Materials
Balloons
Large needle or bamboo skewer
Mineral oil

Safety Precautions
Wear chemical splash goggles and always follow laboratory safety rules while performing demonstrations.

Demonstration
Blow up a balloon and tie it off. Do not fully inflate! Dip the end of the needle or skewer into the oil. Using a gentle twisting motion, insert the needle into the thick nipple end of the balloon and continue pushing until it re-emerges just next to the knot. The balloon should not burst. Pull the skewer out and the balloon will deflate. Repeat with a second balloon, this time try inserting the skewer in the middle of the balloon. It will burst.

Disposal
Throw balloon away in trash.

Reference
Sarquis, M.; Sarquis, J. *Fun with Chemistry: A Guidebook of K–12 Activities;* Institute for Chemical Education; University of Wisconsin: Madison, WI, 1991.

Making Rayon

Prepare a synthetic fiber from natural polymers.

Application Organic Chemistry • Consumer Chemistry • Polymers

Theory Schweitzer's Reagent is a solution of copper hydroxide in strong ammonia and contains tetraaminocupric ions. Schweitzer's Reagent is used to determine whether a fabric sample is made from natural or synthetic materials. Wool and cotton will dissolve in Schweitzer's Reagent, while synthetic fibers such as nylon or polyester will not. Cellulose is a natural polymer and will dissolve. The dissolved cellulose is regenerated when placed into an acid solution, which destroys the basic tetraaminocupric complex. This regenerated polymer is called cuprammonium rayon and is significantly less crystalline than the original cellulose.

Materials

Cupric sulfate pentahydrate (25g)	Magnetic stirrer
Ammonium hydroxide, 15 M, NH_4OH (165 mL)	Büchner funnel
Sulfuric acid, 0.5 M, H_2SO_4 (300 mL)	Filter flask
250-mL Beaker	Forceps
600-mL Beaker	Syringe or pipet
11-cm Filter paper circles (4)	Distilled or deionized water
25-mL Graduated cylinder	250-mL Graduated cylinder

Safety Precautions Wear safety goggles. Ammonia liquid and vapor is very irritating to eyes and skin and toxic by ingestion and inhalation. Use a fume hood while working with ammonia, it is a serious respiratory hazard. Sulfuric acid is severely corrosive to eyes, skin and other tissue; considerable heat of dilution with water; even very dilute solutions are harmful to eyes and skin. Cupric sulfate is a skin and respiratory irritant and is toxic by ingestion and inhalation. Wear chemical splash goggles, chemical-resistant gloves and a chemical-resistant apron.

Preparation Using the magnetic stirrer, dissolve 25 g of $CuSO_4 \cdot 5H_2O$ in 100 mL distilled or deionized water. After solution is complete, place under a fume hood and slowly add 13 mL of 15 M ammonia solution. Filter the precipitate of cupric hydroxide using a Büchner funnel and filter flask. Use an aspirator to provide suction. Discard the filtrate. Wash the precipitate with several small portions of distilled water. Again with stirring, dissolve the washed precipitate in 150 mL of 15 M ammonia solution—use the fume hood. Shred the filter paper circles and add them to the ammonia solution. Keep stirring. The filter paper is the source of the cellulose, and it will dissolve in about two hours.

Demonstration Place 300 mL of 0.5 M sulfuric acid solution into a 600-mL beaker. Draw up about 5 mL of the Schweizter's Reagent solution into a syringe or pipet and add to the sulfuric acid solution. A dark blue thread of regenerated cellulose (rayon) is formed. Remove the thread using forceps, wash the thread thoroughly with water and dry on a paper towel. It may now be handled.

Disposal Neutralize the ammonium solution using Flinn Suggested Disposal Method #10. The excess sulfuric acid can be used for the neutralization.

Reference Alyea, H. N.; Dutton, F. B., *Tested Demonstrations in Chemistry;* 6th ed.; Journal of Chemical Education: Easton, PA.

Smart and Stupid Balls

Show how temperature can change the properties of a polymer.

Application	Polymers • Physical Properties • Organic Chemistry
Theory	Even through the balls look alike they are made of different polymers. The Smart Ball is made of cross-linked polybutadiene. The Stupid Ball is made of a block co-polymer of poly (styrene-butadiene) or poly (vinyl-butadiene). These two balls are virtually the same size and volume but have slightly different densities, both of which are greater than water. They are both black but have a slightly different appearance in that one (smart) is shinier than the other. The dull one (stupid) has a slightly sticky surface. You may notice that the stupid ball is easier to squeeze. The most interesting comparison is their response to being dropped from the same height above a solid surface. One bounces like a super ball (smart ball) and the other stays put (stupid ball). If both balls are placed in boiling water, they will both bounce. If placed in a freezer, the stupid ball becomes even less elastic and will not bounce at all.
Materials	Smart/Stupid Balls, 2 pairs, available from Flinn, AP1971 400-mL Beaker Hot plate Water Tongs or oven mits
Safety Precautions	Wear chemical splash goggles and always follow laboratory safety rules while performing demonstrations.
Preparation	Place one pair of smart/stupid balls in freezer overnight.
Demonstration	Bounce the two balls from the same height. The smart ball will bounce like a super ball while the stupid ball will not bounce. Heat both balls in boiling water. Allow the balls to come to the boiling temperature. Bounce the balls from the same height again. Both balls will now bounce. Place both balls in freezer overnight. Drop both frozen balls. The stupid ball becomes less elastic when frozen and does not bounce at all.
Disposal	None required.
Reference	D. A. Katz, Cabrini College, Radnor, PA.

Index

Index

Index

Index

Index

Index

Index

Index

Index